The Carrion Vine

WORLD WAR II SIBERIAN PRISONER'S SAGA REMEMBERED

*"Its beautiful flower belies the putrid smell. The bountiful
ball of fruited berries is poisonous – its creeping tendrils quietly
envelope everything which grows around it.
Like Communism itself, beautiful at first glance,
offering plenty for all, it quietly corrupts all
who live near or beneath it."*

Jan Wozniak

Frans Elizabeth Reilly

Library of Congress Control Number: 2007910115
ISBN: 9780615180427

For information, and orders:
Call: (815) 338-0211
Email: eescully25@att.net

Designed and printed by Hahn Printing Incorporated
752 N. Adams Rd., Eagle River, Wisconsin 54521

First Edition, Eighth Printing

PROLOGUE

Nancy Howard Jung

To my knowledge, this story has never been told. No trace of it can be found in the history books of World War II. When the Iron Curtain of Soviet Russia clanged down, it shrouded all traces of Russia's usurpation of Eastern Poland, while the world's attention was focused on Hitler's atrocities.

Like the insidious, deadly carrion vine whose creeping tendrils envelope everything in its path, the Soviet Russia of 1939 slowly and surreptitiously invaded its' neighboring countries stifling hundreds of thousands of Polish, Jewish and Slavic families. Millions were uprooted and sent into secret labor camps all over Russia.

This story deals with the fate of the residents and refugees who fled to that region to escape the German invasion of Poland.

A true story of the wife of a diplomat living in Switzerland, and her fourteen-year old daughter, it is suitable reading for teenagers as well as adults.

Vita Kew and her daughter Ellie were vacationing in Western Poland when they were captured by the Russians, while fleeing from the Germans at the onset of World War II. Caught up in the drama of changing political boundaries and the vagaries of war, they were shipped to a Siberian labor camp with hundreds of thousands of Polish citizens, as Communist Russia began to expatriate the countries along its Western border. Their story is written in a docu-drama format, because Vita's diary, upon which it is based, was understandably incomplete in many details, and some incidents were sketched from Ellie's memory only. Above all, however, this is a sincere and thrilling story, told with a clear voice.

While the subject matter is sometimes grim and awful, the tale itself is full of hope and humanity punctuated with poignant, sometimes even humorous vignettes of the stalwart group of Vita's and Ellie's friends...and enemies.

The fact that they survived is due to their spirit of indomitable courage, cunning and endless creativity. It is truly a story of survival.

Only now, in the light of the recent freedom in Poland has the magnitude of those deportations come to light.

More than fifty years later, the world is finally beginning to hear of these hidden labor-prison camps, and the question is being asked: What happened to the millions of people who disappeared behind the Iron Curtain?

These people survived the carrion vine of Russia due to their own ingenuity, but what of the countless others?

AUTHOR'S NOTE

The Carrion Vine is a historically accurate, non-fiction account based upon the diary my mother kept, fleshed out with my vivid memories as a 14 year-old girl.

It is written in a narrative style, in the third person, like a short story. I began writing in a diary –type style, but it became too hard, too emotional and too personal for me to continue. I had to remove myself and look at it from an observer's standpoint and recount all the events objectively as if they were happening to someone else.

Also, some of the character's names have been changed at their request to protect those who are still in Russia.

Our story is representative of the unspeakable treatment of hundreds of thousands of innocent people by the Russian government. It is accompanied by photos and a detailed map tracing the journey from Warsaw, Poland to Siberia and the ultimate return via central, then southern Russia, over the Caspian Sea to Persia and then to India.

MY SPECIAL THANKS TO...

My very good friend Nancy Jung for incessantly spurring me to write this story and helping me put together the piles of notes and diary fragments into the final manuscript.

My much loved Dennis Scully, for his help with his superb knowledge of the English language and editing talent.

To Jim Parker and B.J. Frantz, for their special computer expertise, and my circle of faithful friends, Ed and Jacque Stokes, Tony and Rosemary Bellion, and my newest neighbors/friends Lillian Braidwood, Marie Splinter, Nancy Moore, and a group of published writers, whose compliments and encouragements inspired me to print this true story.

And finally to my mother, for her meticulous and detailed diary, kept secretly with constant fear of discovery, without which, these pages could not have been possible.

So, Mother, as promised – here it is.

TO MY MOTHER – MY INSPIRATION

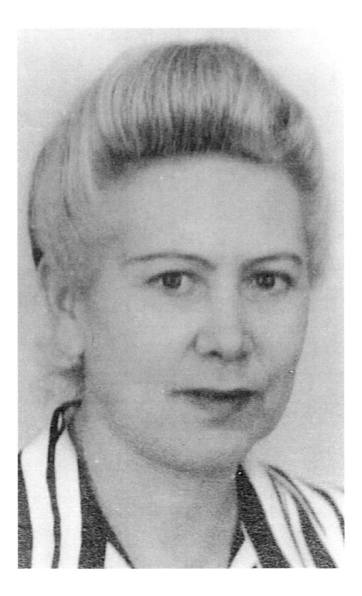

CHARACTERS

ON THE ROAD	AGE	ON THE TRAIN	AGE
Paul Francis Ernest Kew	39	Jan Wozniak (Univ. Prof.)	34
Vincentina (Vita) Kew	36	Maria Wozniak (Jan's wife)	29
Erane Elizabeth (Ellie) Kew	14	Krista Wozniak (daughter)	8
		Elzunia Wozniak (daughter)	3
Anton von Baur (Paul's uncle)	65		
Alma von Baur (Anton's wife)	62	Greta Karowska	?
Peter von Baur (younger son)	26	Anya (Greta's daughter)	16
Alex von Baur (older son)	35		
Anna von Baur (Alex's wife)	33	Stan Kucharski (laborer)	40
Wanda von Baur (daughter)	13	Marta (Stan's wife)	40
2 von Baur children (younger)	?	Marian (son)	15
George Dubczyk (truck driver)	36	Jerzy Czerny (orphan)	16
Tanya Dubczyk (George's wife)	30	Nella Czerny (orphan)	12
Eugenia (George's mother)	60	Dorotka Czerny (orphan)	8
3 Dubczyk children	8, 6, 2		
		Mr. & Mrs. Kos (store owners)	65
Ivan Nadvorny (Polish writer)	40		
Tekla Nadvorny (Ivan's wife)	37	Dr. Bernard Helman	38
Greg Nadvorny (son)	14	Sarah Helman (Bernard's wife)	?
		Helman Son	?
Bogdan Kowalski (Ivan's neighbor)	?	Helman Daughter	?
Sonia Kowalski (Bogdan's wife)	?		

IN THE CAMP

Igor Ivanovich Smolenski   45
   (Camp Vozempka Commandant)
Valeria Yevgenovna (Igor's wife)   ?

Boris Fyedorovich Sokol   50
(Igor's replacement)

THE CARRION VINE

1

LIFE BEFORE

"Although Hitler has already taken Austria and Chechoslovakia, no one in the diplomatic circles takes him any more seriously than a small general posturing for power."
Paul Kew

June, 1939.

It was a lovely day in Mid-June, 1939. The school year was almost over, report cards all handed out, the children spilled out of the classrooms in noisy groups heading home. A very good report card clutched in her hand, 14-year-old Elizabeth ran home as fast as her spindly legs could take her. She couldn't wait to show her straight A grades to her parents and confirm the yearly plan of her trip to heaven! Heaven was a large Arabian horse-breeding farm in Western Poland she was allowed to visit every year since she was ten years old. The farm belonged to her father's uncle, Anton von Baur, whose life was horses. His farm was a large establishment, well known for the pure Arabian bloodlines. It was a product of inheritance after his father's death; Anton had added a line of Anglo-Arabs and Trakehners in response to the Polish government's need for cavalry mounts. The farm prospered with this new addition resulting in lucrative government contracts and a substantial income.

All breathless and excited, Elizabeth barged into the house waving her prized papers at her parents. Her mother signaled her to be quiet as she listened intently to her husband's side of a telephone conversation, her needlepoint canvas in her lap.

There was a lot of this kind of talk that particular year. Elizabeth was not quite ready to understand her parents' worrisome preoccupation with the political situation in Europe and great concerns with the growing power of Hitler, Chancellor of Germany. There were rumors of high-level diplomatic endeavors by several countries to do everything possible to prevent another hostile move. Elizabeth could not imagine what that meant, she also could not see why all this should interfere with her yearly vacation at the farm.

Paul Kew finally put down the phone and, looking much relieved, explained that things were looking up, diplomacy was working, and efforts were being made to calm things down and put heavy pressure on Hitler to behave himself.

Vita Kew gave a big sigh of relief and, turning to her daughter, said: "Ellie, was there something you were going to tell us?"

Ellie handed her the papers she was holding and waited for a reaction. "Why, my dear, these grades are wonderful – look Paul, all As and even the deportment grade is better this year." Paul got up and, giving his daughter a big hug, said: "Well done, Ellie – congratulations." Ellie then wanted to know whether plans were being made for her holiday trip to Poland. They both agreed that the situation was still precarious, but they would certainly give it a serious thought.

Vita Elizabeth Kew, at age 36, thought of herself as an accomplished, well adjusted woman. As an only child of rather elderly parents, she was given every advantage a young woman could desire. After finishing her schooling, she married a young diplomat, Paul Francis Kew, choosing him wisely, she thought, over other prospects. He was an attaché at the Polish consulate in her home town. Well educated and very self-sufficient, he impressed her as a stable, responsible young man, multi-lingual and with a great sense of humor.

His father, Jordan Kew, was an English horse trader, making many trips to Poland to the von Baur farm, buying pure bred Arabian horses for his customers in England. There, he fell in love with Anton's sister Teresa, and never went back home again! They were soon married and Jordan became a welcome right-hand man at Anton's farm. When their son Paul was eight years old, Teresa died of consumption. Grief stricken, Jordan followed a few years later. Young Paul became Anton's ward and was given much love, care and a good education. He decided to go into the diplomatic service which, he thought, would provide him access to different European countries, particularly his father's England he was so determined to see and learn about.

Vita loved her life with Paul. They traveled. His diplomatic posts took them to Berlin, Copenhagen and Rome for two-year periods. Now, almost five years in Switzerland, Paul was rising rapidly. Diplomatic service had been good to them. They lived well and enjoyed the amenities attendant to Foreign Service.

Vita's only real concern was her daughter. Ellie, at fourteen, was a skinny, wiry, freckle-faced redhead, full of pranks; she was a hopeless tomboy. Vita often wondered what would it take to have her daughter eventually mature into a proper, well-behaved young lady.

Paul was no help at all in these matters. Ellie was the son they did not have. He took her to his club's sports car races and hill climbs, taught her to drive at age eleven, and secretly relished the Mother Superior's report that Ellie and a young classmate had put honey in the holy water fonts at the entrance to the school chapel, and then giggled uncontrollably at the nuns' dismay. He also loved it when the maid found her hated peanut butter sandwiches stuck to the dining room wall, behind the paintings. She had him wrapped around her little finger, quite aware of his weakness and took full advantage of it. He was no disciplinarian. That part of her upbringing was left entirely to Vita, who had to put her foot down on many occasions, handing out restrictions and punishment, sometimes over his objections.

And the clothes! There was always a struggle between mother and daughter over what a young girl should wear. Vita believed that habits of good grooming, proper behavior, and all the other graces were a mother's duty to instill in a daughter at an early age.

"Look at you," she would say when Ellie came flying into the house after school, knee socks down at her ankles, blouse pulled out of her skirt, hair partly unbraided and a glint of mischief in her eyes.

"What's the matter, Mother? I ran all the way home from school – I'm late for my riding lesson!"

With that, she would bound up the stairs and quickly change into her favorite attire – riding breeches, boots, sweater – then down again at full speed, past her mother still standing at the bottom of the stairs helplessly shaking her head. In a matter of seconds, Ellie was out of the door calling to her friend in the waiting car that would take them to the local stable. Vita could never understand her daughter's fascination with this smelly and rather dirty activity of grooming, saddling and finally riding a horse. But Ellie seemed to live for it. Where did that come from? Certainly not from her – she was a city girl all her life and the furthest thing from her mind would be living in the country, on a farm among peasants, away from......

She shuddered at the thought. But her daughter marched to a different drummer. Unfortunately.

These yearly trips to the von Baur farm in Poland seemed to be what her daughter dreamed of all year long. Vita remembered their first trip when Ellie was just ten. She would get up at five with the hands and work with them as they groomed, fed and exercised the animals. She was stepped on and squashed against the walls of their stalls, but even that didn't slow her down. At dinner, all she could talk about was what the new mare, Natasha, had done; how the foals were running beside their mothers now; and how she hoped the shots would help Old Jusef's fetlock infection.

Uncle Anton looked at her with pride in his eyes. "Vita dear," he would say: "this girl is taking after me! One day, when she is a little older, I will give her one of my champions! What do you think of that?" Dear Lord – thought Vita, that's all we need.

August 8, 1939. So here we are again, thought Vita, as the car that picked them up from the railroad station rolled slowly over a rutted road leading to the farm. After all the arguments, persuasions and mitigations, and Ellie's crying tantrums and in spite of Vita's apprehensions and fears, here they were, approaching the gate. The main house was just ahead. It was a large stucco building, white with brown beams, not unlike an English Tudor, but simpler in line and feeling. It had two wings. Alex, one of Anton's sons lived there with his wife Anna and their three children. Their daughter, Wanda, was Ellie's age. His other two children were six and four. Peter, Uncle Anton's younger son, lived in Torun and attended university there, seemingly forever! He would spend weekends and holidays at home.

"Oh look, Mother, There are Uncle Anton and Wanda!" Ellie shouted in her ear. Anton, looking trim and fit for his age in his faded breeches and scuffed boots, flung the car door open and literally dragged Vita from her seat in a crushing bear-hug. Ellie jumped out the other door and raced to embrace Wanda.

Anton was a tall, strong man who smelled perpetually of cigars, leather and horses. His big walrus moustache had grayed a bit, Vita thought, as the breath rushed out of her, but he hadn't changed much since she last saw him. He was still the lovable old curmudgeon he always had been, and so what if he was a bit boring at times? He's entitled, she reasoned. After all, hadn't he raised two sons almost by himself? You couldn't really count the forever-sickly Aunt Alma. Hadn't he taken Paul in and reared him as his own son when Paul's parents died? Paul's mother was Anton's only sister who had died at an early age and her grief-stricken husband had followed a few years later. It was his duty to rear and educate his nephew and he had done a fine job.

"Vita, you look wonderful! How is Paul? You must tell me everything. Haven't seen you in a whole year. Come in, come in! Adam, bring the luggage!" he boomed, encircling her shoulders with one great arm and ushering her into the cool house.

Vita spotted Aunt Alma sitting on a couch, wrapped in a shawl, with a flyswatter in her hand.

Aunt Alma, it's so good to see you again," she cooed, sitting down beside her. "How have you been?" Alma smiled wanly and coughed. It was a plaintive little bid for sympathy. "Oh, I have really had a very bad winter, and I don't seem to have enough strength to get better. Those migraines…"

"Oh, horse feathers!" interrupted Anton, "all you need is to get out of this house into fresh air and sunshine. Where are you going?"

Alma rose, pursed her lips into an expression of resignation and replied. "Please excuse me; I cannot bear these house flies. Anton, the least you can do is see that the servants get rid of them in this house.." She began to climb up the stairs coughing dryly to accentuate, appropriately for Vita, her tenuous grasp on life.

There was no doubt about it, Vita thought, Aunt Alma was a miserable creature, constantly suffering from migraines. She hated the country, complained about everything and everybody. Nobody paid much attention to her.

2

THE WINDS OF WAR

*...Suddenly the word 'war' would fall from radio speakers
casting claw-like shadows over the lazy, warm August days ...*

August 12,1939. Life on the farm settled into the usual routine for the von Baur family and their guests. Anton, concerned with the daily business of running the farm, Aunt Alma mostly upstairs suffering from another imaginary ailment, the girls riding, playing with the horses, helping with chores and generally having a wonderful time.

Vita spent her days quietly reading the several books she had brought along, doing her needlework and, to her own amazement, rather enjoying the tranquility of country life. To break the monotony, she would often make trips to the neighboring town, sometimes alone or with Anna and the girls. Adam, who doubled as the family driver, would take them in. At an arranged time, he would pick them up, usually in time to make it back for dinner. Vita enjoyed walking the streets, doing some shopping, having coffee in a sidewalk cafe, picking up the local paper and reading the news.

As the warm August days went by, her trips to town became more frequent. There was something in the air, something un-palpable, yet very real. Although people went about their business as usual, there seemed to be a feeling of anxiety and unrest. Small crowds would gather around corner kiosks reading the front page headlines and talking to each other. Others would stop a while to listen to a news broadcast from a radio someone had set up in an open window. Suddenly the word war would fall from the speaker casting claw-like shadows over the lazy, warm August days, sending shivers through Vita. She could see young girls holding on tightly to their young men's arms, bewilderment and anxiety in their eyes. She must call Paul, she decided. This really wasn't a very good idea to come here this year. It was sheer foolishness to give in to a fourteen-year-old and separate the family at a time like this.

Back at the farm, after dinner, Vita excused herself and went to the telephone to make her phone call to Paul. She placed it with the long distance operator and was warned that it might take some time to get through to Switzerland. She swore under her breath at the poor Polish telephone service and the inefficiency of the operators. It wasn't until 11:00 p.m. that the operator finally rang and completed the connection. Paul sounded calm and reassuring. The situation really was not as desperate as Vita imagined. All efforts were being made on the diplomatic level to keep peace. As a matter of fact, Paul said, he was planning to fly in earlier than originally anticipated and was looking forward to some rest and relaxation. They said their goodbyes on a much happier note, and Vita hung up the phone feeling reassured and confident that Paul knew the situation probably better than anybody and would certainly know what to do if there was any imminent danger of war. She went up to bed feeling much calmer.

August 19,1939. While the family gathered for their customary coffee and sweets in the middle of the afternoon, the girls ushered in a welcomed visitor.

"Grandpa, Peter is here!" announced Wanda, hanging on to the young man's arm.

"Peter? What the devil is he doing here in the middle of the school week?" Anton wanted to know. Peter, his younger son, was attending the university in Torun, taking some extra summer courses. He was tall and handsome and enjoyed his academic life to the fullest. He greeted everybody with hugs and kisses and settled down to a cup of coffee and a huge slice of cake.

"Well," said Anton, "what's up?"

"Oh, nothing much. I just wanted to talk to Alex and you, Dad, if you have a minute."

"Well, let's have a smoke in the office."

The three men walked into the adjacent room, and Peter slid the large pocket doors closed behind them. There was no other way for Peter to break the news but to come right out and confess.

"I have quit school and have enlisted in the army. Half of the university is doing it also. We are just waiting for our orders."

Anton's shock passed quickly and gave way to a tirade of arguments against such a foolish decision.

"Peter! Leaving school, enlisting! That's the most stupid thing you could have done. I know it looks like Hitler is ready to start something again, but we have a ten-year non-aggression pact with him, signed, when was that, 1934? We are also strongly allied with France and Great Britain; they promised to defend us if Hitler makes a move!"

"Father, Father, you are not thinking rationally," interrupted Alex. "Look what Hitler has gotten away with up till now! What about how he took Austria and Czechoslovakia? What did the British and French do then? Sure, they expressed 'grave concern,' but did nothing! We are next, Father, there is no doubt about it. All those diplomats can do is talk, but that's all it is, talk. We are dealing here with a mad, power-hungry man, can't you see? He wants the corridor and Danzig back. He is not going to stop now, even if it means World War II!"

"You are wrong," insisted Anton. "Hitler may be mad and overambitious, but he is shrewd enough to know he can't win."

Peter interrupted him again. "You do know, I am sure, what is happening along our entire western border. German troops, tanks and artillery are all there, ready to attack! And speaking of that, we are so close to the border, it would be wise for you to make some kind of plan to get the family onto safer grounds and move some of the stock further east."

"You are crazy!" Anton replied. "I am not moving anywhere! And I would advise you two to calm down and make sure you don't upset the women and children. All we need here is panic!"

With that he marched out of the room. The two young men sat in silence. Finally, Alex got up from his seat with determination and said, "I don't care what father says, I am getting Anna and the children out of here before it's too late."

"I think that's a wise move," agreed Peter. "Let me know if there is anything I can do."

****

August 24,1939. The radio and newspapers were the only source of information Vita could get now. Her last three phone calls home either did not go through or she wasn't able to reach Paul. She was listening to the latest bulletin mentioning casually that the German Man-O-War Schleswig-Holstein had sailed into the Baltic Sea and positioned itself right across from the Westerplatte Peninsula. But, the commentator stressed repeatedly, it was just a "courtesy visit." No need for concern.

The girls came running noisily into the house having been down at the stables. Every day, after their riding lessons, they were permitted to watch the mares and their foals as they were gathered together and led to the stables. It was always the most wonderful time of the day. As each mare was led into the wide aisle, two grooms would grab her foal and put a small halter on him and "handle" him gently. They would run their hands up and down the foals' legs, stroke their heads, rub their bellies, pat their rumps. They would put their fingers in the foals' mouths and gently pry them open.

"This is to get them used to accepting a bit, later," explained one of the grooms.

They would walk around them patting them at all times, holding their tails so that the foals would get accustomed to being touched all over without any fear. Then they would lead them up and down the aisle under the watchful eyes of the mares, who also were being groomed in cross-ties by a pair of boys. Some young fillies and colts were already so "gentled" that the girls were allowed to lead them on their own. The babies were then rewarded with a lump of sugar and, after a good brushing, led into their stalls with their mothers.

"What's going on" Why is everybody so gloomy?" asked Ellie. She put her arms around Uncle Anton. "Oh, you would have been proud of me today. I learned the side-step on Natasha, and...."

"Ssssh," interrupted Vita, "we are trying to listen to the news."

Ellie made a face and, motioning to Wanda, skipped out of the room.

****

August 26,1939. The news was just as confusing as the entire situation. First, a general mobilization of the Polish Army was declared, then for some reason, called off. The rumor was that the Polish government was under a lot of pressure from Britain and France to stop mobilizing; not to anger Hitler and provoke him into action. The two young von Baur men received their notices to report to their units, simultaneously with the cancellations, but decided to go in anyway, to at least find out what was going on. Alex made arrangements with his in-laws in eastern Poland to house his wife and children when it became necessary for them to leave. Peter kept unsuccessfully urging his father to do the same.

Vita was glued to the radio. The call now came from the Defense Department for all able-bodied men to report to their units, with an explanation that there was no need for panic.

"We just want to be ready, in case....It's better to be prepared....Nothing will probably come of it....The men will be back in no time....No cause for alarm."

And the telephone circuits were so overloaded, she could not call out anywhere.

****

3

THE FLIGHT

...Over and over the voice of Torun's mayor could be heard on the radio with urgent advice to move the women and children east, away from the cities. Announcements of special masses in churches and cathedrals were broadcast. Pray for peace! was the final word ...

August 30, 1939. Ellie and Wanda went along with Alex's wife, Anna, to the city to do some marketing.

The town was in turmoil. Crowds of people were milling around, many uniformed men gathered on the streets; large lorries loaded with soldiers were passing through, heading out of town. Newspaper headlines proclaimed general mobilization again, and yet, business was as usual. Anna went to the building designated as headquarters for the gathering soldiers, but couldn't see her husband anymore. Somebody told her that he was already shipped west, toward the German border. She gathered the girls, who were at a pastry shop, and they all rode home in silence. The entire situation seemed gloomy and frightening. When they got home, Uncle Anton met them in an agitated state, explaining that Vita had just received a call from Paul in Switzerland urging her to make immediate plans to either fly back or take the train home. Paul had told her to contact Hans Schmidt at the Swiss Consulate in Torun, who would help her get reservations. He was still quite optimistic that the diplomatic efforts of France and Great Britain and even Italy would sway Hitler and prevent a world disaster, but felt it wise for his family to get back home as soon as they could.

Maids were already gathering their things and helping Vita pack. The house was in turmoil. Aunt Alma, weeping, offered to help. Anton tried to reassure the children. With none of his usual fuss and sputtering, he talked away their anxiety, soothing them as he might a pair of new foals. But, at that moment, a car pulled into the driveway and he left them to greet a neighbor, Mrs. Kozlowska, and her daughter, Hanka.

After a brief greeting, Mrs. Kozlowska announced, "We are on our way to Bialystok to stay with my sister until this blows over. We will stop in Torun for a day or so to pick up some things and close our house there. What are your plans? Where are you going?" she asked Anton.

"We haven't made any plans as yet," he answered, taking her coat and offering her a chair.

"What!" she exclaimed. "You have not made any plans? Do you realize what is going on out there?"

"Well, Vita and Ellie are getting ready now. They will leave sometime tomorrow. Alex and Peter have already joined their units, and Anna and the children will go to stay with Anna's parents in Wilno."

"And how about you and Alma?"

"Alma may go with them if she feels well enough. Look, I am not going to argue with you. I am just too old to run. Besides, most of my hands were mobilized, and I am not leaving my horses behind. I was born here — this is my home and this is where I stay!"

"Oh, that's very smart. Horses! Is that all you can think about at a time like this? The government is urging civilians to evacuate all areas close to the border."

Alma and Vita now joined the two visitors.

"What do you mean — evacuating people?" Vita asked.

"Oh, Mother of God!" said Alma.

"Now, just a moment," interrupted Anton seeing the panic on the women's faces. "Where did you pick up such nonsense?"

"Nonsense?" Mrs. Kozlowska exploded. "Don't you people listen to the radio?"

Vita was just turning it on. Somebody was making a flowery speech, then a Mozart symphony came on.

While the maid, with the help of Wanda and Ellie, was serving coffee, the music was interrupted and rapid announcements were made of designated mobilization areas, depots for military issue, departure times for military trains, and evacuation instructions for the civilian population.

"Well, there you are!" said Mrs. Kozlowska. She turned to Vita, "Did you get a reservation?"

"Not yet. I couldn't even get through to the Swiss Consulate. I am really very worried. I don't know what to do!"

Mrs. Kozlowska took charge.

"Why don't you both come with us right now. There is plenty of space in the car. You can spend the night with us in Torun, and then in the morning it will be much easier to make arrangements from there."

Vita accepted the invitation gratefully, in spite of Anton's protests.

"I was planning to drive you in tomorrow morning," he said.

"I know," said Vita, "but this is a much better arrangement. You can come tomorrow with the luggage and see us off. We will probably have our reservations by then."

Vita went upstairs to get their coats and small bags. Ellie, shaken and stunned by the speed of this departure, started to cry.

"Please, Ellie, I want you to stop this minute! There is no time for tears. I need you to help me with the bags, then I want you to change your clothes. Your things are laid out on your bed. Wash your face and hands, comb your hair and behave like a fourteen-year-old young lady should!"

"Yes, Mother," she ran upstairs tears streaming down her face.

It just didn't make any sense! She was so looking forward to her father's visit. There wasn't going to be any war!

When they were almost ready with their packing, Anton called to them to hurry down. They ran to the sitting room just in time to hear a message from the Mayor of Torun. He urged all civilians not to panic, to limit their phone use to emergency calls only, to make an effort to move all women, children and elderly from the cities in an easterly direction, away from the German border to the safety of villages, fields and woods. He stressed that the move should be orderly and calm — there was no danger, it was just a precaution. There was a heavy concentration of German armies along the border and, in case of any incidents, he wanted the civilians well out of range.

Vita shot Ellie a meaningful look. The girl was now visibly frightened.

"Uncle Anton, what will you do? What will happen to the farm and all the horses if...?" she asked.

"Now, now, don't you worry about that, Anna and the children are leaving tomorrow morning, and I will wait and see what happens. This might all blow over."

Mrs. Kozlowska stood up, shook her head in disbelief, and, after a round of goodbyes, led the group out to the waiting car.

"He is such a stubborn old codger, there is just no use. He will not move!" she muttered.

Anton and the rest of the family walked to the car for a final farewell.

"I will come up tomorrow morning with the luggage and see you off," said Anton.

"Grandpa, can I come too?" asked Wanda.

"Sure, sure."

****

Ellie could not speak during the ride into Torun. It all was happening so fast. She was not too young to understand the seriousness of the situation. She was holding back tears with all her might, glancing furtively at her mother. Vita, lost in thought, sat quietly in the spacious back seat smoking one cigarette after another and watching the pastoral Polish countryside slip by. The only thing missing from the tranquil scene was a kite in the sky.

Vita remembered the kites. Great colorful wedges with streaming tails. Paul would design and build them meticulously with Ellie's help and, if the weather was right, there would be an expedition to the park that weekend. Vita would pack a roasted chicken in a picnic basket with some wine and cheese and other goodies.

Ellie could never wait. Even before the car had come to a complete stop, she would be out the door with the new kite, running across the grass as fast as her spindly legs could carry her, playing out string to the zigzagging kite. She could never quite get them airborne by herself and they crashed, time and time again into the ground. When she could run no more, she would return to where Paul and Vita had spread a blanket and collapse.

"Father, please," she would beg. "The wind is just perfect, but I can't do it alone."

Paul was tall and strong. His laughing smile made him seem much younger than his thirty-nine years. The few silvery grey hairs at his temples were hardly noticeable among the windblown curls of thick, dark hair. He sat easily on the blanket arranging knives and forks over napkins so they would not blow away in the breeze.

"Help your mother, Ellie, and then we'll see if the new bird will really fly."

He would smile and rumple her long auburn hair as his daughter hastily emptied the contents of the hamper, afraid the wind would die down before they had a chance to run the kite to the end of its line.

A few giant strides from Paul's long legs and the kite was aloft. While Ellie tugged for altitude, Paul would carve the chicken and serve everyone. The remainder of the afternoon would be spent lazily watching the brilliant speck dancing high in the bright blue sky. Paul loved the kites and Vita loved the afternoons.

****

They came at last to the high iron gates of the Kozlowski house. It was located in the southern outskirts of the city, close to the Vistula River. Two big Dobermans yipped a welcome to their mistress. Vita wondered if it wouldn't be wise to go immediately to the Swiss Consulate to see whether some arrangements had been made for their departure.

After the car was unloaded, Emil, the driver, took Vita into town. Schmidt wasn't there any more, but his secretary contacted him at home and Vita had a lengthy conversation with him. He assured her that going directly from Torun to Bern would be quite impossible. Her best bet would be to take the train to Warsaw where a variety of transportation was still available and, in fact, he had obtained reservations on an express train leaving August 31st at 4:00 p.m. He was, however, still working on the possibility of obtaining reservations on a direct flight from Warsaw to Bern, but that was not available until September 2nd. He strongly urged Vita to take the train next day, and she wholeheartedly agreed. He planned to meet her next morning and deliver the tickets to her personally. Paul was a good friend of his, and he would do the best he possibly could for his family.

Vita felt much better. She would call Paul in the evening and tell him that she and Ellie would be arriving on September 1st.

Mrs. Kozlowska made them comfortable in the guest room and, after the girls were sent to bed, the women took their coffees into the library and spent the evening listening to the radio, which now broadcast nothing but patriotic songs, speeches and public information; the same urgent advice to move women and children east, away from cities; announcements of special masses being held in churches and cathedrals. PRAY FOR PEACE! was the final word.

Vita tried and tried to call Bern, but the circuits were all busy and finally at midnight she gave up. No matter, she thought. She could manage very well once they crossed the Swiss border. Just to get there!

****

August 31, 1939. Vita slept badly and woke early, tired and apprehensive. She got up, making as little noise as possible, so as not to wake Ellie, and when Mrs. Kozlowska knocked on their door, she was already bathed, made up and on her third cigarette. She had also packed and repacked their cases several times. All their traveling clothes were laid out. Money, jewelry and the passports went into her brown crocodile handbag, the largest she owned. She would wear the matching shoes, high heels, but quite comfortable, and her brown Maggie Rouf suit. Annoyed, she noticed she had brought the wrong hat!

For Ellie, her navy skirt, white sweater, her navy boycoat and hat, navy knee socks and Oxfords. Vita strongly believed that the way you looked and spoke determined the way you were treated by the world, and for this long trip home they would look their very best! Left to her own devices, Ellie would have worn her scuffed riding boots and breeches.

Breakfast was brought on trays to their room. Mrs. Kozlowska supervised the setting up and then joined Vita with a fresh cup of good, strong coffee and a cigarette.

"Ellie, get up, take your bath and get dressed. Breakfast is already here!"

Mrs. Kozlowska then told Vita there was a message from Hans Schmidt. He was sending their tickets by messenger sometime before noon. The best he could do was two first class seats to Warsaw and then rail connections on to Bern via express line. He said that airline reservations from Warsaw out of the country were now non-existent. It would be a long journey, but it was all he could do under the circumstances and no small accomplishment at that. It was a minor miracle, in fact, considering that he had managed a first class compartment on the last train that would take civilians. He also advised that they should get to the station in plenty of time. The train was scheduled to leave at 4:00 p.m. The connection from Warsaw to Bern was not until the next day with departure at 5:30 p.m. He apologized for the inconvenient timetable, but this was the best he could do.

Ellie bathed and dressed, listened to Mrs. Kozlowska's report, nibbling on a sticky bun and drinking her juice.

"Now, what am I to do all day, Mother?" she asked.

"Practice the piano!" snapped Vita, in no mood to pursue this any further.

She made several attempts to call Bern again, but couldn't get through.

Shortly before noon, Anton arrived, with Wanda and the luggage. Mrs. Kozlowska, with a maid in tow, was setting up a lunch of bread, sausage, cheese and tea. When the girls went out to play in the garden, Anton began to talk about his worries — the horses. Anna, the children and Alma were all ready to go to Anna's parents, but he had to stay behind to take care of his valuable mares and stallions. Not only did they represent a huge, life-long investment, they had to have care.

"How am I to manage," he asked indignantly, "with the boys and my best hands called up and everybody else running off? And then there are the yearlings — already bought and paid for — government property, and the two- and three-year-olds, almost trained and ready for delivery, but I have no instructions and nobody to drive the vans! Well, what am I supposed to do? The breeding stock, that's my problem, but who will be responsible for the government horses?"

Mrs. Kozlowska excused herself and went out shaking her head. Vita, her thoughts far away, sat with the old man, drinking tea and smoking, until it was time to go. The girls were called in and Ellie, muddy and flushed from romping with Wanda and the dogs, was sent up to wash her face and hands and do up her pigtails.

"Your coat and breton are in the hallway. I want you back here, looking decent, by the time I count to ten," said Vita.

"I will take you to the station," said Anton.

"No, no," Vita replied. "The bags are already in the car. Emil can help us if there are no porters. You must get back to the farm."

And then the goodbyes started — hugs and kisses and more hugs and promises, Uncle Anton saying, "No porters? What nonsense! Well, safe journey! Give my love to Paul. Until next year!"

Vita thanked Mrs. Kozlowska for her help and hospitality. She was very grateful.

"Yes, next year," said Vita, getting into the car.

Emil snaked his way slowly through the heavy traffic, pedestrians and vehicles of every description. Torun was in chaos! Military vehicles everywhere. Trucks and cars jammed with people inched their way through narrow streets. Emil, thank God, knew the town very well and managed to skirt some of the clogged streets, using alleys and side streets. The confusion was a terrifying cacophony as they pulled up to the station. The station itself was pandemonium where a few policemen and some officials with armbands tried to direct the crowds to their trains — there were now several of them loading simultaneously. Emil forced his way into a first class car and waved through the window.

"Over here, Madam, over here!" he shouted.

With difficulty they pushed their way through the crowd, and he lifted Ellie up the steps.

"Your compartment is No. 3. Just show your tickets to the conductor. I will be right back with your bags."

Somehow they found their way to the assigned seats, two of them across from each other by the window. Emil handed them their small bags through the open window and then came back with claim checks for the rest of the luggage. Vita tried to press some money into his hand, but he refused to accept it, wishing them a good journey and waving to them as the crowd swallowed him up.

The day was unusually warm and the compartment stuffy, in spite of the open window. All seats were now occupied by a variety of people — two elderly couples, a single young mother with a two-year-old toddler, a distinguished-looking, well-dressed man and two young girls, perhaps twenty years old, probably university students. Vita wondered, observing them, who were they and what brought them here and where were they going? Her thoughts were interrupted by one of the men saying, "Well, I guess we're off!" as the train laboriously got under way.

Ellie shed her coat and hat and tugged at the warm turtleneck of her sweater under the disapproving glance of her mother. All the others sat stiffly, maintaining the decorum appropriate to their red-plush surroundings. There was no conversation. Wishing she had a book or newspaper, Vita smoked. Ellie, by the window, watched the landscape slide by, astonished at the numbers of people on the roads, in every kind of conveyance, or simply walking along the tracks. Occasionally another train would pass going in the opposite direction loaded with soldiers, hanging out the windows, waving their hats and shouting greetings.

They had been traveling less than an hour when the train stopped, backed up, lurched forward and stopped again.

"What's the matter?" asked one of the ladies.

"They are switching us onto a siding," said her husband. "I am afraid there will be a delay."

"But we will miss our connection," she said, furtively glancing at the other passengers. "Anybody else making connections in Warsaw?"

"We are," replied Vita, pointing to her daughter," but not until tomorrow. I have no idea where we'll stay or what we'll do until then."

"Oh, dear, our children are meeting us in Wilno. I just hope we can catch another train. There is such chaos everywhere. Jan," she called to her husband, who now, with a couple of other men, was standing by the open window in the passageway trying to look out. There was nothing to see but an expanse of fields and woods.

Shortly thereafter, the conductor came through, harassed and irritable, to announce that the delay would probably be a long one. The passengers all protested at once, showering him with questions.

"I am sorry," he finally got his word in, "all rails are being used for military transport, and that has priority!"

"Is the dining car open?" asked Vita.

"There is no dining car!" he stated bluntly and went on.

It was, by then, about six o'clock and having had just a very small lunch at Mrs. Kozlowska's, she started to wonder when and where they could get some food. The two university students were on their second candy bar, and Vita could not help but notice Ellie's glances at the disappearing chocolate.

"Mother, didn't Mrs. Kozlowska give you something for us to eat? It's in your bag."

"Of course!" Vita had completely forgotten the package Mrs. Kozlowska pressed on her, saying, "Here, Vita dear, I prepared a snack for you. God only knows when you will get a decent meal."

She reached for her handbag and brought out a small sack with cheese, biscuits, fruit and candy. Unpacking the food, she glanced around at the other passengers, wondering how far her supply would go if she offered it to the others. She extended her hand with the food and offered it to the lady sitting next to her, who thanked her and brought out her own hamper with some food.

"See," she said, "we came prepared! Here, please help yourselves."

She offered her sandwiches to the other passengers. A thermos with coffee appeared from somewhere; somebody opened up a tin of cookies; one of the men offered cigarettes, lighting them for the ladies, and so, over the food they all seemed to relax a little, talking to each other, commiserating and wondering what tomorrow would bring.

It was past midnight when the train got under way again. Most of the passengers were now dozing, but the men talked in undertones, each expressing his views on the current situation, each having a different opinion. Vita listened attentively to their arguments not knowing much about the Polish government, its leaders and politics in general. One of the men was positive that war was inevitable. Others disagreed — the same old story, just like Uncle Anton's dinner table — talk, talk, talk. She finally dozed off also and awoke to realize that the train was standing still again, waiting. She pushed the window curtains apart to see dawn streaking the sky over the Polish countryside.

****

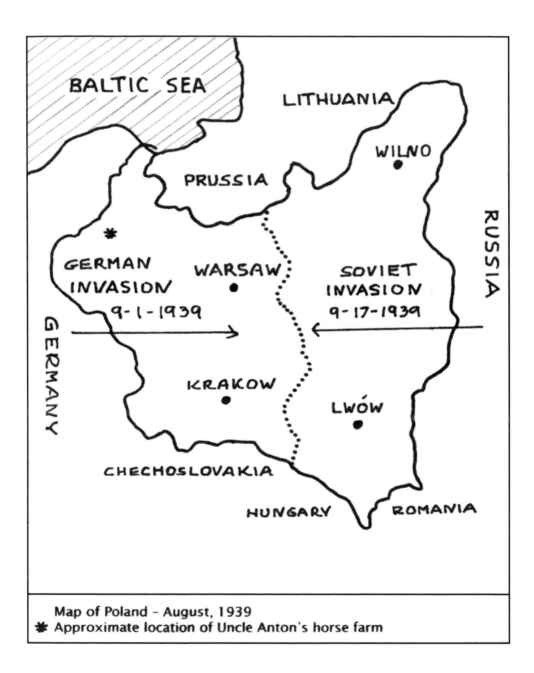

Map of Poland – August, 1939
✳ Approximate location of Uncle Anton's horse farm

4

AND SO IT BEGAN

Blitzkrieg! Germany invades Poland.

...As the clever hopes expire of a low dishonest decade:
waves of anger and fear circulate over the bright
and darkened lands of the earth.
                    September 1, 1939, by W.H. Auden

September 1, 1939. In the isolation of their first class compartment, no one knew that the war they'd argued about had already begun. While their train sat idly on the sidelines, their whole world was collapsing around them.

At 4:15 a.m., this day, September 1, 1939, the German man-o-war, Schleswig-Holstein, on its "courtesy visit," had opened its eleven-inch guns on the Polish positions in Danzig harbor and the Westerplatte Peninsula.

There was some resistance from fifty-one Polish postal workers barricaded in the post office building. The German Storm Troopers blasted their way into the building and, spreading gasoline all over the defenders, set it afire. All fifty-one Poles burned to death. Half an hour later at precisely 4:45 a.m., Hitler struck all along the 1,750 mile Polish border. The Fourth Army smashed through the disputed Polish Corridor, other units pushed through to the Vistula Plain toward Warsaw, other armies struck Silesia marching toward Kracow. One and a half million men followed the twenty-seven hundred Panzer tanks moving with incredible speed all along the Polish border.

By nightfall Danzig had, said its local Nazi leader, "returned to the Great German Reich."

In the air the new German Junkers-87 Stuka dive-bombers blasted roads and rails. They were equipped with a fiendish new device — the bombs which emitted screams as they fell on their terrified victims. And then, the heavy droning Henkel IIIs in squadron formation could be heard as they headed for Warsaw. That same morning almost the entire Polish Air Force was destroyed on the ground in a surprise attack with just a few planes lifting off in a desperate effort to mount a defense. The Germans called this new warfare BLITZKRIEG!

****

But the train passengers had no idea of what was happening around them. In their innocence they organized and tidied up their belongings in anticipation of the train's arrival in Warsaw. They never made it to the main railroad station, because it simply wasn't there anymore.

One of the women, leaning out the window, stifled a scream.

"Oh, God, look at this!"

A mangled sign, "WARSZAWA," that had once been affixed to the building's wall, now only said WAR. The significance of those three letters had little impact on most, but the few who had some knowledge of the English language were overcome by its prophetic meaning.

Warsaw station had evidently been hit very early, because portions of some of the buildings, which could be seen from the train window were now rubble, some of them on fire, belching flames and smoke. The main hall was still intact, but was inaccessible through the debris. The passengers were ordered to disembark. This train was not going any further. There was no time for goodbyes. They all stood there on the platform among piles of luggage, which the handlers were tossing out doors and windows. Vita found a couple of her bags. The rest, even if found, would be impossible to carry. It was almost too difficult for them to move through the mobs of confused and panicked civilians mingled with hundreds of soldiers, only slightly more organized, some in uniform, some just carrying their gear, waiting to be told where to go and what to do. They stood aside to let a group of reservists march through — excited country boys, flowers pinned to their lapels, singing and shouting: "On to Berlin!"

"We must find the Swiss Embassy," said Vita after the first shock of fright subsided. "Ellie, stay close to me. Let's find a cab out there, on that street."

They half-carried and half-dragged their belongings, moving slowly out of the station to a tree-lined street across from a park. But, of course, there were no cabs anywhere, so they inched their way down one street, then another, thoroughly confused.

"I can't carry all this anymore," wailed Ellie. "What are we going to do?"

"Please don't cry. We will find some place to rest and repack some of the things — now come along," urged Vita.

In her chic Parisian suit and her alligator shoes, she moved steadily along as if she had some definite destination in mind, and everything would be all right when she reached it. She was just about ready to stop a passerby to ask for directions when a loud siren started wailing.

"Oh, dear God, it's an air raid!" she realized.

Everyone on the street scrambled in different directions. Vita, shouting to Ellie to stay close, made a mad dash for the park and the safety of large trees and thick bushes surrounding a fountain. They had barely reached the trees when sickening, screaming noises sounded here and there, followed by ear-splitting explosions. One here, two there, several a little further away. Ellie had a death grip around her mother's waist trying to hide her head under the jacket. She closed her eyes very tightly, but couldn't keep her teeth from chattering.

"Oh, oh, here they come again!" she cried.

They heard the roar of the planes as they made another sweeping turn and headed for the remaining part of the station, some buildings surrounding it, and the general residential area along the railroad tracks. Then fire engines and other emergency equipment came rushing to the scene. A couple of lonely anti-aircraft guns positioned on one of the rooftops popped a few shots now and then at the low-flying planes. There was the sound of a child crying, people calling to each other amid the paralyzing screams of the falling bombs, again and again followed by explosions. Ellie was crying. Her mother stroked her head and held her close.

"Mother, look here. There is blood all over," she sobbed holding up her blood-covered hand.

"My God, are you hurt?"

"No, I don't think so. I think it's my nose."

"Oh, for Heaven's sake! Don't worry about that. Nosebleeds are not fatal! Here, turn around, lie down and put your head in my lap — it will stop in a little while."

She extricated a handkerchief from her bag and pressed it against Ellie's nostrils.

"Hold on to this — it will be all right. Look here, you've got blood all over my clothes!"

"I am sorry," whimpered Ellie. "I don't like to look up like this. I will see the planes."

"Close your eyes. I think the raid is over for now."

In a few minutes the all-clear sounded from a nearby tower and people started to move around the small park. Vita got up, went to the fountain and, not having any cloths or towels, wet a few pages of a newspaper left on a bench and wiped Ellie's face as best she could, but when the blood-soaked hankie was removed from the nose, the blood kept flowing.

"It's still doing it! You said it would stop!" shrieked Ellie.

A man stopped by and suggested Vita put pressure on both sides of the nose and hold it for a while. She pressed both her thumbs on either side of the nose and held them there it seemed forever, but as soon as she let go, bleeding began again. She found some cotton in her cosmetic case and, rolling two tampons, packed the nose as tight as she could. Nothing. The blood kept oozing through the cotton.

"It will never stop. I will probably die!"

"Now, Ellie — nobody has ever died from a simple nosebleed! Just calm down. It will stop."

She was reassuring the girl, but began to worry herself. What will I do if this keeps on, she wondered. After a couple of hours she decided to see if anybody knew of a nearby hospital or a doctor's office. Somebody pointed out a building at the end of the street and said that there used to be a pharmacy there — maybe it was open. She admonished Ellie not to move and ran across the street, found the building housing a small pharmacy. The door was locked. She pounded on it and rang the bell until a window opened above the store and a gray-haired man leaned out.

"Are you a pharmacist?" she asked.   "Yes, what can I do for you?"   "I have a child over there in the park with a terrible nosebleed that has lasted a couple of hours and we can't stop it. Is there anything you can do?"

"Just a minute." He came downstairs to open the store door. "What happened?" he asked. "Was she injured?"

"I really don't know. We were hiding in the park during the last raid and it just started bleeding."

"Probably concussed," he guessed.

Vita was talking to the man, but her eyes wandered from shelf to shelf noticing all the items she thought she might need. The pharmacist gave her a few ampules with liquid in them.

"You should actually inject this stuff," he said, "but it will also work taken orally. Give her one of these now and another later this evening. Where are you staying?"

"That's a good question. We came here on the last train from Torun to make connections to Bern on the express leaving late this afternoon, but as you can see, we are not going anywhere. I suppose we will stay in the park, unless you know of a hotel?"

"No," he said. "I would ask you in, but my wife and I are leaving Warsaw in a couple of hours. I have already closed my store and we are packing. You are welcome to take a couple of blankets, if you intend to spend the night in the park. It's probably safer than in any of the buildings."

Vita bought some aspirin, soap, a bag of candy, two tins of crackers, cigarettes and was told that a bakery and a grocery store were just around the corner. She ran back to the park, gave Ellie the medicine, cleaned her up a bit and left her again to run over to the small neighborhood store for some food. She had barely made it back to the park when the sirens started howling again. The raids came one after another, some bombs falling quite close, some a distance away. Quite a group of people had gathered in the small park by nightfall. They decided to spend the night there, using the benches and lawns. Ellie's nose finally dried up and she gingerly moved around, fearful that any sudden jar would start the bleeding again. They spent a very uncomfortable night on a park bench, wrapped in the pharmacist's blankets.

****

September 2, 1939 – Bern, Switzerland. Paul Kew was on the phone again with his friend Henry Kohler at the London Embassy office.

"I am not able to get through to the farm anymore, Henry. I am really quite frantic! You got any news or suggestions?"

"Well," replied Kohler, "as you well know, the invasion is on. No formal declaration of war, and Hitler is saying he is defending his troops from attacks by the Polish Army. There have been some incidents along the border. Don't know any details. I also hear that the Polish government is frantically mobilizing. It's a little late, isn't it? In the meantime Bonnet, Deladier, Chamberlain and Lord Halifax are pussyfooting, trying desperately to avoid involvement."

"But Henry," interrupted Paul, "they have pledged to defend Poland. They have an obligation."

"Yeah, I know, I know. I understand they are delivering an ultimatum to Ribbentrop, some time tomorrow."

"Tomorrow?"

"Yes, France is apparently not ready."

"Oh, God! I guess there is no hope. I have got to do something. I have two defenseless women out there, and there are no flights to Poland anymore."

"Paul," said Kohler, "try the Red Cross. I understand they are shipping medical supplies to the front."

"Of course!" Paul slapped his forehead. "Why didn't I think of it? I have a very good friend there. He is president of the International Red Cross."

"Well, there you are," answered Kohler. "Good luck and keep me posted."
They rang off.

****

September 2, 1939 – Warsaw. The morning would have been sunny and beautiful if
it weren't for the fact that at 6 a.m. a siren signaled another approaching raid.

Oh, God, we have got to get out of the city, thought Vita. We will all be killed if
we keep sitting here!

A radio could be heard from one of the windows across the street — an
announcer saying something about a German invasion all along Poland's western
border, Nazi troops marching in with little or no resistance. He urged the civilians
to move East. The rest was drowned out by a distant, heavy drone of approaching
aircraft. Vita gathered the blankets and packages and pushed her daughter into
some heavy bushes. They burrowed into the side of a small hill, holding on to each
other, waiting. Then the first eruption came from quite a distance, then another,
then a succession of them, each closer and louder than the previous one, and then
they were overhead. Ellie closed her eyes tight until they hurt and covered her ears
with both hands.

"Why are they doing this?" she hissed. "I hate them!"

Vita made a decision right then. When the raid was over, they were moving on.
They would walk or crawl, but they would not sit helplessly waiting for the next
bomb to fall on them. Anger rose in her. She was an innocent bystander. This
wasn't even her home, her country. What went wrong? Why was she here to begin
with? What did Paul think sending her and Ellie into this insanity?

The last series of bombs fell on the already half-destroyed railroad station, a large
hotel, and some official buildings on the other side of the park. And then the
planes were gone. In the ensuing cacophony of fire engine sirens, ambulances and
all-clear signals, Vita hastily packed up their belongings, urging Ellie to help. They
were going to leave the city; it would be much safer in the open country. There
would not be as many strategic targets for the Germans to bomb, she thought.

****

It was another warm, clear day, unusual for September. Later they would call it
"Hitler Weather." Clear skies, good visibility, mild temperatures. Mother and
daughter, overloaded with luggage and packages of food made little progress.

"This way Ellie," Vita urged. "Let's follow the crowd."

And so they fell into step with the others trying to keep up. Progress was slow.
Everyone carried or pushed something: a cart, a wheelbarrow, a baby carriage.
From shattered windows, undecided, others watched, but with every mile the crowd
grew. They did not make way for civilian vehicles, but parted for army trucks and
cheered, the soldiers cheering back. Here and there the mob eddied around a

shop, picking up some food or other supplies. People gathered also at churches, in front of police stations and wherever a radio could be heard, although there was little to hear except repeated instructions to move women and children out of the city. The remnants of the Polish army were also instructed to retreat eastward, to establish a second defense front.

And after each short broadcast, Chopin's Polonaise was played, as if to show that Poland still lived.

The larger suitcase became too heavy to carry. In spite of many rests and Ellie's help, Vita's arms gave out. She could no longer drag it.

"Where are we, Mother?"

"I don't know."

She sat down on the edge of her valise, helplessly. All the streets looked almost alike. After the last air raid, parts of the sidewalks were uprooted and large piles of rubble appeared here and there. Some of the buildings stood with their innards hanging out, while others were slowly burning, belching black smoke into the clear, blue sky. Here and there a wall of a building split neatly open exposed the insides of a grocery store with some shelves still intact. A row of sausages hung in an orderly manner over a counter. All that was missing was a white-aproned grocer waiting on his trade.

"Oh, Ellie, be careful."

Vita was too tired and weak to get up from her perch. Ellie scrambled over a heap of rubble and found herself inside a confectionery store.

"Oh, yoo-hoo," she shouted repeatedly. There was no answer. She was very thirsty, looking for water, but couldn't find any, so she filled her pockets with chocolate bars and stuffed her mouth with two large creams.

"Mother, we should take some. There is nobody here."

"Sweetheart, we can't carry the things we have."

"Oh, I can carry the candy!"

"I bet you can," Vita smiled.

She made a decision to repack the cases once more and dispose of everything that was not essential. Her feet were killing her in those heels. They would have to go. She would keep one change of warm sweaters, coats, throw out the hats, silk blouses and dresses. She observed other people on the road. They all carried knapsacks on their backs leaving their hands free to carry other bundles. If she only had one of those.

They found an empty vestibule in a once-fashionable, small hotel, which now looked like Grand Central station. Doors stood ajar, people milled about the lobby, all trying to get checked out as fast as possible, before the next air raid would trap them there, maybe forever. Vita and Ellie changed their clothing, repacked their bags leaving the bulk of their belongings behind, and set out once more onto the street, their step much springier, their loads lessened considerably.

Well, this is much better, Vita felt. Ellie had her riding clothes on, a wool sweater and a jacket. Vita wore low heels, skirt and jacket, one of Ellie's berets on her head and a raincoat over her arm. Ellie laughed heartily over the makeshift knapsack. Vita stuffed a pair of breeches with clothing and odds and ends of food and other small items and fitted it on Ellie's back. Two belts served as suspenders attached to the two leggings turned under her arms. It was a sight, but she could now carry a heavier load easily and still have her hands free to help with the other bundle which Vita wrapped into a large square scarf. They left the hotel, heading in an easterly direction.

The weather couldn't have been nicer. It looked as if the Nazis and St. Peter had joined forces against the Poles. A typical September day would have been rainy, foggy and cold. This fall, however, was exceptionally nice. Balmy weather, clear blue skies, unlimited visibility. Bombing was easy, targets visible, strafing a game! Pilots could spot a crowd of people running, seeking shelter and they could fly low, zero in on them and mow them down. Then they could sweep up into a large loop, turn, come back and do it again! They could have this fun almost at will, until their squadron leader would call them back into formation to head home to refuel and reload. The next morning they would be back again!

"There is another small park. Maybe we can rest a bit? I am also very thirsty."

Ellie ran ahead across the street to a fountain house. A group of people were sitting in clusters under the huge chestnut trees, resting their legs. In the center of the park a young boy, maybe 15 or 16 years old, was selling sandwiches, coffee and ice cream.

"There is a smart kid," remarked one of the travelers. "He will make a fortune!"

"Oh, what good coffee." Vita relished every sip.

The people gathered there were all trying to run away from the bombs. They seemed stunned by the sudden vicious attack, confused and frightened by the conflicting news and orders that came to them in snatches over the radio. Some said the city should be evacuated. Others beseeched them to stay and defend Warsaw against the approaching Nazis.

A man, sitting dejectedly on the ground, leaning against a tree kept saying: "I can't understand this. How is it possible that we have no defense plans of any sort? Where is our anti-aircraft artillery? Where is our army? What the hell is the government doing about all this? We have had our freedom for 20 years only. Is this it? Is it all over, again?"

He looked around at the circle of tired, dejected faces expecting some answer, some explanation, but there was none. He waved his arms disgustedly and, heaving himself up, walked, hunched over, across the street into a building.

"Do you suppose it's safe to stay at a hotel overnight?" someone asked.

"Oh, sure, nights are safe. The sons of bitches don't bomb and strafe in the dark. Just make sure you are up and out early in the morning," someone else said.

****

September 2 – Night. The small nearby hotel into which Vita and Ellie had entered was clean and nice. The proprietor wasn't sure if he and his family would stay in Warsaw, but as long as the building still stood and there were so many homeless people on the streets, he would stay open. After their baths and a hot meal, Vita and Ellie turned in for a good night's rest. It was heaven to stretch out in a real bed instead of a seat on a train or a park bench like the previous nights. Sleep came fast.

"Mother, please put on the light, there is something biting me!"

"What do you mean, something biting you?"

"Well, I don't know. My whole body itches like crazy!" Vita snapped on the light as Ellie jumped out of bed, ripped off the covers and examined the bed carefully. There was nothing there, clean white sheets. She lifted the pillow and spotted a black round bug scurrying with great speed under the mattress.

"What was that? Did you see it?"

"Nooo." Vita was too tired to care. "Probably a flea."

"A flea? It was as big as my thumbnail! I am not going to sleep in that bed!"

"All right, all right. Do you want to sleep in my bed? I will change with you."

Anything, Vita thought, just let's get some rest. No sooner did they settle down, the lights came on again. This time Vita was sitting upright, scratching her arm.

"You are right. There is something biting here!" A big welt appeared on her arm.

"I bet those are bed bugs!"

"Bed bugs? What are bed bugs?"

"Well, I don't exactly know, but they seem to live in the cracks of furniture and walls and live off blood, just like fleas, I suppose."

"Oh, yuk!" Ellie was out of bed and getting dressed. They spent the rest of the night with the lights on, which for some reason intimidated the bugs, sitting in chairs, trying to get some sleep.

****

September 3. A thunderous noise jarred them awake. They had evidently overslept because the sun was already rising and another raid was in progress.

"Did you hear the sirens, or did we sleep through them?" asked Vita, scurrying around, picking up their things and pushing Ellie out the door. Thank God we are dressed, she thought.

They ran down the long hallway toward the stairs when an ear-splitting explosion sent them flying against the wall.

"You all right?"

"Yes, yes, let's go!"

They scrambled down the stairs to the main floor dragging their belongings, but couldn't get through the lobby. Panicky crowds jammed the exit trying to get out. Part of the hotel was now collapsed and one could not see through the dust.

Some man grabbed Vita by the arm and yelled into her ear. "Over here, over here; there is a side door!"

They were stepping over overturned furniture, bricks and lumber. They could hear screams of people somewhere, but the man kept pushing them on. Climbing over a mound of debris, Vita spotted a bloody arm and hand reaching out from a heap of brick and stone, and a voice cried, "Help, please help me."

Vita pulled Ellie away from the heap and the voice, struggling with the stunned girl, trying to follow her unknown leader. They finally got through a door leading to a side street and ran to the adjoining wooded area where they lay flattened on the ground, while the raid went on. The terrifying bombs which screamed, decreased in pitch as they intensified in volume, were followed by deafening explosions and the rain of falling dirt and debris. And then the planes were gone. One end of the hotel was totally destroyed and starting to burn. The voice from the mound no longer cried, but other voices were now heard groaning and yelling for help. People were lifting timbers and chunks of plaster, searching for survivors or belongings. That raid stayed with Vita in her nightmares. Though she would see worse later, it was that vainly reaching hand she dreamed of, that vainly imploring voice she heard.

****

It seemed they had been walking forever. Some people were picked up by army trucks, and some were lucky enough to find abandoned cars, but most just kept on walking.

"I can go no further. I just can't," Ellie said dropping her bundles on the ground.

"All right, let's rest here for a while. Here, sit in the shade of this car; I will get us something to eat."

They were exhausted. Perspiration caked the road dust on their faces and necks and their hair had dulled to sand color.

"Just look at me." Vita stretched her grimy hands in front of her.

"Do you think we'll ever see Dad again?" asked Ellie close to tears, "or Wanda, or all the others? I keep wondering what ever happened to them."

"Of course we will," Vita consoled. "Don't worry, all we have to do is get to a town that has not been destroyed and find a working telephone or telegraph office, or...."

"Oh, Mother, I am so scared, and it's all my fault. You were so right not to want to come this year." She was now crying, tears rolling down her grimy cheeks.

"Please don't cry. It's nobody's fault, and we will be just fine."

She put her arm around her daughter and squeezed her shoulder. Ellie looked up into her mother's face and saw the worry lines creasing her forehead.

A truck whined up the road in the distance.

5

STRANGE PARTNERS

*...With the Germans Panzers on their heels,
they fled from the bombs, fires and destruction
toward the safety of Puszcza Bialowiejska...*

September 3. George Dubczyk had big square hands. The nails were chipped and broken, the palms calloused. His hands said all one needed to know about George. He wheeled the large produce truck full of family and belongings through the clogged roads, and his knuckles whitened on the steering wheel. Mile after mile, the horror of this unprovoked attack assailed him, and nothing in his experience or his imagination could have prepared him for this assault on his senses. He skirted Warsaw as best he could, but even the outlying areas were not spared. He could see into people's houses where they had been cleaved open as if by some giant axe. Some people were still in them salvaging what they could. He felt embarrassed to stare, but he could not help himself. And the fires...gas explosions...rescuers digging...and everywhere horses, dead horses. He made slow progress, driving around stumbling pedestrians, rescue equipment, burning buildings. He was exhausted. He yearned for the comfort of the hearth and the sweet sound of his wife's voice singing lullabies to the children. He longed for the reassuring sounds of Babka Genia cleaning up after the evening meal. But that was all gone. If they were going to stay alive, ahead of the Germans, there must be no looking back. No past and no future, just today. Right now all of his thoughts were on the fact that he needed gasoline to keep moving ahead. Maybe one day, after this war was over, they could get back....

Out of the corner of his eye he spotted two figures, a woman and a child, sitting on the side of the road, leaning against a car. Maybe, if the car were disabled, he could get some gasoline. He stopped, backed up and got out of the truck. Vita and Ellie stood up as the man approached them.

"Out of gas?" he asked.

"No, this is not my car," Vita replied. "We were just resting here. It seems we have walked forever and we just can't go any further!"

"Where are you going?" he asked.

"I really don't know. Away from the bombs and the German Army, east, I suppose, but mostly I would like to find a working telephone or a telegraph office. You see, we are here alone. My husband is in Switzerland. He doesn't know where we are and what is happening to us."

They both looked so tired and pitiful he could not just walk away. Up until now he had been fearful of picking up strangers. He had to be careful, but not heartless.

"Well," he finally said. "I don't know about the telephones. There is probably no way you can get a line out of the country, but if you like, I can give you a ride as far as you want to go."

Vita almost hugged the man. "Oh, thank you, thank you so much! Ellie, come on. This nice man is going to give us a lift. Isn't that wonderful! My name is Mrs. Kew, and this is my daughter, Elizabeth. We call her Ellie."

"George Dubczyk, ma'am," he said, taking off his cap. "My wife Tania, my mother Eugenia, and our three children back there in the truck. Does this car have any gas in it?"

"I don't know," Vita replied. "We were just using it to rest awhile."

George unscrewed the gas cap. "Let's see how much is in there."

Vita loaded their belongings onto the truck bed while Ellie helped George siphon the remaining gas into a bucket. They poured it into the truck carefully.

His wife brought out some bread and sausage sandwiches, a large container of water, and a bottle of beer for George.

"He doesn't trust the water," she smiled.

"And what are your plans?" Vita asked.

"We are headed for the Puszcza Bialowiejska."

"What's that?" Ellie asked.

"The big woods! Haven't you ever heard of it? Famous place. Rich people from all over the world come to hunt there. The Germans will never find us."

"Oh, Mother, let's go there!"

George took a rumpled map from his coat pocket and spread it on the hood of the truck.

"We are here, still quite some distance from this town, Siedlce. The German Army must be somewhere here by now, maybe even further." He indicated a spot west of Warsaw with a twig. "We do know they will be coming this way as fast as they can re-supply their troops and secure what they have captured. We have got to keep moving. Stay ahead of them. If we can get into the Puszcza, I think we'll be safe. Of course, it's up to you. You are on your own, but that's where we are going, and you're welcome to ride as far as you want. The war cannot last forever. We heard that the English and the French are getting into it also. It's got to end soon. In the meantime, we will be safe in the forests. We might rent rooms with some family, and maybe even hunt bison!"

"Bison!" Ellie said in disbelief, "like the Indians?"

Folding the map carefully, he smiled at her. "Yah, the eurochs. There was a huge herd of them in these woods before the last war. There are not as many of them now. Anyway, these are my plans."

"I don't know," Vita said. "I hear that some of the people are crossing the Rumanian border to get out of Poland entirely."

"Yes," replied George, "but that's hundreds of miles south of here. It would take forever. You're foreign, aren't you?"

"Yes. I am Swiss. My husband is half Polish. His father was English — that's where the name Kew comes from."

"Oh, I see," replied George, "your daughter speaks very little Polish."

"Well, the only chance she's had to learn was during our yearly visits over here. We speak French at home."

"Oh my," he scratched his head, "you sure picked one hell of a time for a visit. By the way, can you drive?"

"No, I never learned."

"I can," Ellie jumped in.

"What, a kid like you? Drive a truck?"

"She can drive anything with wheels," Vita said. "Let her try."

"Why not?" he said.

They all got in. Ellie, George and Grandmother Eugenia in the cab, Vita, Tania and the three Dubczyk children in the back. Ellie proudly took the wheel and demonstrated her competence. The man was delighted.

"Two drivers can make twice as much time," he said and promptly fell asleep.

****

6

AGAINST ALL HOPE

September 3, 1939.
Britain, France, Australia and New Zealand
declare war on Germany.

September 4, 1939. Paul Kew buckled into the seat of a small, twin-engine plane. It had large Red Cross insignia on both sides of the body. He did not know the pilot nor the two other passengers seated across from him. They seemed to be news correspondents, armed with cameras, evidently eager to see firsthand what was happening in Poland.

Paul's arrangements had been made through a friend who owed him a favor, a big favor. The Red Cross would never have allowed him to go as a passenger. Paul's associates at the consulate didn't even know he was going. The only person he informed was his secretary, just in case.... But he had to go. He had to find his wife and daughter.

The plane was so weighted down with crates of medical supplies that it barely cleared the power lines at the end of the runway. Landing on a small grass-covered runway would be equally as difficult, but there would be men to help unload and the return flight would pose few problems with no cargo.

As they hopped off onto the grass, the pilot gave them final instructions. "I will take off at exactly 11:00 p.m. three nights from now. If you are not here, you will be left behind. Remember, eleven o'clock. Be here — and good luck!"

They ran for the cover of the woods as a shadowy crew hastily began to unload the plane. It was gone in minutes.

****

At exactly eleven o'clock three nights later the little plane returned. The pilot whipped the craft around for a fast takeoff as three shadows started across the runway from the woods.

The pilot saw the flash of automatic weapons' fire and soon the three men were surrounded by German soldiers. There were heated words. Their papers were torn to shreds and commands shouted as rifles were raised. The pilot knew the outcome, and he didn't want to watch. He gunned the engine.

The automatics bucked in the hands of the young soldiers. Three bodies jerked and spurted blood as the salvos rang out. For good measure the soldiers jammed another clip into their guns and emptied them into the bodies.

With a final sigh, Paul reached for the tail of the bright orange kite. He caught it and it lifted him off the ground. Higher, and higher, and higher.

****

7

THE TRAGEDIES OF WAR

As early as September 5th, Germany's chief of staff,
Frantz Halder wrote in his journal:
"As of today, the enemy is practically beaten."

Two days later the first tanks of the Fourth Panzer Division
reached the suburbs of Warsaw.

54

September 4-6. They traveled mostly at night. During the day they hid the truck under trees, and if the trees were sparse, they covered it with branches. They slept under the truck or in dense bushes. They did not dare to build a fire, lest the smoke be spotted from the air, so they ate bread, sausage, cheese and food they picked up at farms or an occasional store — canned fruit, vegetables, preserves.

The landscape was changing now. They were out of Warsaw proper, past the outlying residential area. Vita was not convinced that George's plan was the best one for her and Ellie, but she kept her own counsel. For now it was the only alternative. They were riding, not walking, and that was such a relief. And besides, she really had no alternate plan to offer. But she didn't relish the idea of spending a winter in a rented room in the woods, depending on George for food he hunted or fished for. She would bide her time.

Gasoline was their main concern. Vita paid exorbitant amounts for the few liters they found at some of the gas stations that were still in operation, but they were headed toward Siedlce, a large town where Vita hoped to find telephones or the telegraph system in operation. They reached it very early one morning. It was a large town full of activity, refugees, rumors. The people felt fairly safe, since they had heard that the remnants of the Polish Army were now in place, forming a second front, somewhere between them and the advancing Nazis.

Still fearing raids, George insisted on camping in the woods just outside the city while he alone drove into town to forage for food and gasoline. He came back with plenty of food and beer, but with bad news.

"No telephones, no telegraph, Mrs. Kew," he said sadly. "They have been cut off for days. They say that the Polish government is gone! Over the border into Rumania! How do you like that?"

"I think that's the smartest thing anyone could do," said Vita. "I wish it weren't so far away and we could do it too!"

"Well, you suit yourself. I am sticking to my plan. Anyway, I saw a fancy store full of stuff back there, only a little bit bombed. People are helping themselves to everything. I will take the kids. Riding in an open truck, they will need warm clothes."

As they drove away, Vita began to cry, knowing that she would have to go on with him, this ingenious and irrepressible peasant, wherever he took them, because she couldn't bear the thought of going on alone. Tania tried clumsily to comfort her.

When George and the children came back, the truck was loaded. Ellie sported a beautiful lamb's wool jacket, extravagantly embroidered, with a matching hat. The children were similarly attired and each carried an armload of sweaters, socks and boots. He had also picked up two new bicycles, flashlights and batteries, blankets and a bundle of adult clothing.

"Too bad the large sizes were all picked over, but help yourself to whatever fits, Mrs. Kew, and Tania, you too."

Vita picked some clothing out of the large pile and went behind the truck to change. Her suit was a disaster. She quickly tried on a pair of brown pants, a turtleneck sweater, large woolly socks and a pair of boots that laced up the front. She was a sight.

"I wish the girls at the club could see me now!" she joked.

When she came out, she strutted and twirled, while Ellie doubled over with laughter. Even old Eugenia clapped her hands. A woman of Vita's background in a pair of man's pants and boots was a very strange sight indeed!

"Very good," said George.

"It's what they are wearing this year," she said, "in the woods!"

They were all beginning to develop survival instincts.

****

The next morning all hell broke loose! Siedlce was razed off the face of the earth. They had never seen such destruction, such devastation, such chaos before. They were fortunate not to have gone too close to the city itself. They watched from a safe hiding place in a pine grove as one squadron of planes after another dumped tons of bombs on the city. There were fires everywhere. The sky was blood red as far as one could see. George ventured a guess that Siedlce must have been a railroad knot where the regrouping of the remnants of the Polish Army took place, and the Germans wanted to destroy it.

"We will have to skirt around this mess," he said. "Best to go south and then east again."

He had so much faith in his plan and the safety of the deep woods that everybody felt a little better just listening to him.

"You will see," he said, "when we get there. Nobody will ever find us."

When the raids finally ended and dusk settled on the country, they loaded up and proceeded to move, circling the ruins of the city, gingerly picking secondary roads leading south and then east, making as large a circle as possible. Almost the whole city was either in flames or smoldering. The roads were filling up with hundreds of fleeing people. They were all going east, away from the inferno.

George was stopped once in a while and asked to take on more passengers — old women, too weak to walk, young mothers carrying babies, little children tagging along. Vita felt sorry for all of them, but the man wouldn't weaken. He said he couldn't carry any more people, and what difference would it make if he helped one or two? How about the hundreds of others? He finally pulled off the road and pretended that the truck had broken down and waited for the biggest crowds to pass. Progress would have been minimal anyway because of the hordes of pedestrians.

They slept a little, had a meal, this time a cooked one. They made a fire a safe distance from the truck and everybody relished a large piece of boiled Polish sausage, potatoes and lots of coffee. Vita thought with amusement — sausage must be the main staple here because that's all we seem to be eating!

It was so nice to sit around the fire. Once in a while some of the passersby would stop to rest and join them. George tried to get information from them about the roads ahead, the towns they would have to travel through, the location of the German Armies, but most of all how far was his beloved "Puszcza"!

"It's about a hundred kilometers," they would say. "Head due east and you will drive right into it."

As far as the location of the advancing Germans, the reports were conflicting. Some said they were right at their heels; some heard that by now the armies were invading from the north as well; nobody was really sure.

George was anxious to get going. His excitement was rubbing off on all the other truck passengers. Ellie couldn't wait to get there.

"Oh, Mother, won't it be wonderful? We can all live like Robinson Crusoe, out in the woods, gathering mushrooms and berries; and I know how to make a fire without matches, and how to build a shed out of branches. Remember the camp I went to last year? We learned all that! How to survive in the woods! We were there four whole days! At night it was pretty scary because they had bears there, but we made it and it was wonderful!"

The small children listened with awe.

"Bears! Papa, you think there will be bears in our woods?"

"Oh, fiddlesticks! This kid comes from Switzerland. They have different animals there. Here in our woods there will be deer and hare and maybe bison. I know there are also wild boars. Those are pretty nasty, but if you leave them alone, they won't bother you."

Ellie's eyes filled with tears. She cuddled against her mother and whispered, "Do you think we will ever get home?"

Vita had no words of consolation. They just sat there, huddling together until it was time to sleep.

****

When George woke up, the sun was shining brightly.

"Everybody up!" he shouted. "It looks like we can travel during the day today. I haven't heard any planes this morning."

"Do you think it's safe?" Vita wondered aloud.

"Oh, I think so. There is nothing to destroy around here anymore. Why would they strafe fields?"

So they had breakfast, packed up the truck, and started slowly on their way. The roads were rough and getting rougher, so they could make much better time during daylight. It was a race between them and the Panzers who didn't have to stop and siphon gas from disabled vehicles.

Ellie was driving. George would lean out the cab window and talk to the people they were passing. All of a sudden, Ellie noticed some of the people on the road making a mad dash for trees and bushes lining the road, and then she heard the whine of the plane. She swerved the steering wheel to the left and drove off the road, partially into a shallow ditch. George yelled to everyone to take cover. Ellie opened the door and as she got her feet on the ground, the first salvo of shots whizzed over her head. She fell down and rolled under the truck. Vita and one of the children were already scrambling under, all lying face down. George grabbed his oldest girl who was just standing there, bewildered, and dived into some bushes on the other side of the road. He yelled out to see if everybody was all right. Then the planes came at them again. There were two of them. They flew very low, one behind the other. Two more bursts were fired. Then they were gone.

The trucker spat out a string of curses. "You God damned sons of bitches!" He was seething, his fists clenched, his face contorted.

"Mother, you all right?" yelled Ellie.

"Yes, I am fine."

"Are the children all there?" asked Tania. Slowly they all dared to crawl out of their hiding places. The planes were now far away.

Two of the older children were crying loudly and their mother tried to hush them. Everybody was looking for the baby and calling his name, but he was nowhere to be seen.

"Oh, Jesus, where is he?"

George and Vita got onto the tailgate of the loaded platform and froze in horror. There, under some bundles, was the bullet-ridden body of George's mother — a forgotten member of the family. Nobody had thought of her. She was lying face down over the blood-soaked body of the child. She looked as if she wanted to shield the baby from the bullets. George gently moved her over and extricated his little body from under the weight of her body and some pillows and odd pieces of luggage. He was covered with blood, his hair all streaked and stuck together. Evidently when George held him in his arms, the baby must have stirred or made a noise, because he put his ear to his chest and whispered, "My God, he is alive!"

He jumped off the tailgate and gently laid the little boy on the ground.

"Quick, get some water!"

They all made a dash for the large milk can that contained their supply of water. Vita grabbed some rags and a towel. They kept washing the blood off his head, his hands and arms, but no wounds appeared. He finally came to and when he took a look at his blood-soaked clothes he started screaming.

"Grandma, Grandma!"

The short-lived joy at the boy's survival was soon over — Grandma was dead. There was no doubt about that. She must have been hit by several machine gun bullets. They had made a grizzly path up her spine, and then up through some luggage and through the cab roof, in a straight line. George picked up some of the blood-stained blankets and folded the body in them. He didn't know what to do next. The little boy's only injury seemed to be a large knot on his forehead, otherwise, after a thorough cleansing and a change of clothes, he was as good as new.

It's a miracle," wept Tania. She knelt on the ground to say a prayer. The other children followed her, their hands folded and their eyes raised toward heaven.

"As long as you are at it, say one for Mother," George said bitterly.

He was leaning against the truck, his head in his hands. Vita walked over to him and tried to console him. He finally pulled himself together and started to think logically. what do we do now, he wondered. Go back to Siedlce with the body and try to find someplace where his mother could be buried?

Vita suggested that maybe they could bury her right here, in the field, but he wouldn't hear of it.

"No, I better take her back. We can't travel on with the body; I have to take her back!"

They all decided to set up camp in the nearby stand of pines while he drove back toward town. It wasn't that far. Vita didn't like the idea of getting separated, but his mind was made up. Ellie was cleaning up the broken glass from the shattered windshield and windows in the truck's cab. As she looked ahead onto the hood, she noticed several holes running toward the front of the "nose."

"Mr. Dubczyk, please come here. Look at this."

She pointed to the hood. He ran up and nervously lifted it. The engine was shot in more ways than one! The bullets had pierced the radiator in several places, went through the head cover, the carburetor. It was a mess. When they looked under the truck, the ground was soaked with water and oil. A feeling of despair came over all of them.

"Oh, Christ, what now?"

George was seething with anger. His wife and children stood back as he beat his fists on the fenders and yelled obscenities. Vita finally had had enough of this display and in a firm voice put an end to the tirade of foul language.

"Now listen here," she said. "We are in a very difficult predicament. All your tantrums will not help us any, so let's calm down and decide what to do next. We have got to use our heads."

She handed him a bottle of beer, and they all sat down on the ground in a circle. She suggested that he ride one of the bikes back to the last farm house they had passed the night before. Maybe the people there could help, maybe he could buy a couple of shovels. She dug into her large bag and took out 200 zlotys and handed them to George.

"When you come back, we will dig a grave right here. I am sure some of the people walking by will help us. This is the most appropriate place for Grandma to be buried. This is where she died, just like any soldier, a victim of this horrible war," she talked fast and convincingly.

George finally agreed. Yes, this was the only thing they could do. After getting some food into him, they sent him off with blessings and promises that they would be just fine without him. After he was out of sight, Vita organized the little group to get their things unloaded, so they could spend the night under the pines. They took blankets, food and clothing off of the truck and carried them to the campsite. The bicycle came in handy. It was much easier to put a bundle onto the seat of the bike and roll it down the path than it was to carry it on their backs. Pretty soon only Grandma's body was left on the truck. They busied themselves fixing a meal, ate it in silence, and then Ellie and Vita went to gather wood for a fire. They almost gave up hope of seeing the man back that evening. They had no idea how far he would have to go. Traveling at night, as they had been up to this morning, it was hard to see anything beyond the truck's headlights. There could have been farms or houses not too far away or maybe he would have had to go as far as the outlying areas of Siedlce.

The fire was now lit, and the women were making up some bedding out of the blankets and trying to get the small children to settle down for the night. They would take turns, Ellie included, watching the fire. Vita brewed up a pot of strong coffee and took the first watch. Ellie insisted on staying up with her. They wrapped a blanket around their shoulders and settled near the fire, sipping their coffees.

"I wonder what Dad thinks happened to us?" said Ellie. "He must be terribly worried."

"I am sure he must be," replied Vita. "If we could only find a place where we could send a wire or even a letter, or make a phone call just to let him know that we are alive."

All of a sudden she was overcome by a feeling of self-pity. What had she done to deserve this? Why should she go through this all alone? Why couldn't he be with her? After all, he was the head of this family! Bitter tears stung her eyes.

"Do you think we will ever see him again?" she heard Ellie whisper.

Now she felt ashamed of herself. She put her arm around the girl's shoulders and, hugging her with all her strength, tried to sound very strong and convincing.

"Certainly we will, sweetheart. I promise you we will!"

Tears choked her and all she could do was tighten her grip around those thin shoulders and hang on. Right here in her arms was the reason to survive, to weather this war, and to make every effort to get her small family reunited again. She could do it! She had to!

****

George rode his bike down the dusty road, deep in thought. There had to be another way. Burying his mother along the road and leaving her there where stray dogs could dig her up was unthinkable. It was almost more than he could bear.

"Hey, where are you going?" The voice shocked him out of his reverie. "You can't go back there. The Germans have taken Siedlce, or what's left of it."

"No, I am not going back there. Can you tell me how far it is to the next farm or village?"

"It's only a few kilometers, but...."

He waved to the group and rode on as fast as the rutty road would let him. After a while he could see the roofs of several farm buildings surrounded by a cluster of trees. He rode up to the gate in the white picket fence. A woman was taking her laundry down off a long line and he greeted her. She came up to the gate, and he asked her if he could speak to one of the men folk.

"They should be back from the field pretty soon for their supper," she replied. "If it's water you want, the well is over there. Help yourself."

"No," George said. "I just need to get some help."

He proceeded to tell her his story. She felt sorry for him and invited him inside to wait for the men. In about an hour they came back, riding in a large wagon pulled by a pair of heavy work horses. There was an older man, two younger ones and a boy.

"This is my husband, my son and grandson," the woman said, "and this is our farmhand."

George didn't waste any time. "I hope you can help me. I am willing to pay for it."

With that he pulled out 100.00 zlotys out of his pocket and laid it on the table. The men eyed the money and then the man suspiciously.

"What is it that you want us to do for this kind of money?"

George explained hastily that his mother was killed in a strafing raid and he wanted to give her a decent burial. There was another 100.00 zlotys for the priest if they had one in the nearby village.

"Well, where is she?" the younger man asked.

"Just a bit down the road. We were in my truck when we were strafed. Now it's useless."

The farmers thought it over and wanted to know how badly damaged the truck was. George anticipated their thoughts.

"Listen, if you can use the truck, you are welcome to it. It is badly shot up, but I am sure it can be fixed."

The men had a quick conference. Yes, they could help him, but not tonight — there were chores to be done — but if he was willing to stay overnight, they would give him a hand in the morning.

George was very grateful.

"Thank you so much. God bless you," he mumbled.

Presently they and other members of the family sat down to a very big meal. Looking at the table with all the food on it and the calm and gentle faces of the family sitting around it, no one would ever guess that there was a terrible war going on out there — cities leveled, people dying, thousands fleeing the enemy — yet here, all was calm and quiet. After supper, the men sat around the hearth in the large kitchen, peacefully smoking while the women cleaned up the dishes. George told about his flight and about the Swiss lady and her daughter whom he had picked up on the way. He didn't know much about the war, only some rumors he heard from the people.

"Lord only knows where the Polish Army is or the Air Force. How can a supposedly well-armed country collapse in three days? It is inconceivable!"

"We hear that Warsaw has not given up, they are keeping the Germans out," one of the young men said.

His father shook his head sadly. "Son, it's only a matter of time."

****

George was put up for the night in the kitchen on a long bench close to the hearth. Sleep didn't come to him easily. He tossed and turned, the day's events heavy on his mind. He was anxious to get back to his family and see to their safety.

The farmers got up with the first rooster's call; the samovar was started, fire rekindled, and the smell of fried bacon filled the whole kitchen.

After a large breakfast and many cups of strong coffee laced with milk, they made preparations to go, leaving the morning chores to the women. A simple coffin was nailed together out of several pine boards and loaded onto a wagon together with George's bicycle. A pair of horses was then hitched to it. Another pair was prepared to be ridden or led, their heavy leather pulling harness stored in the wagon. One horse was haltered and a long rope was handed to George who was sitting on the back of the wagon. The young lad rode the other, saddled horse. He was to go ahead to the neighboring village to let their priest schedule the funeral.

"Now, Stas, you know what to tell Father Gorski when you see him? We will go slowly so you will have plenty of time to catch up with us, and don't run the mare too hard. She will need her strength to pull the truck back."

"All right, Father," said the youngster and was off down a dusty side road.

It seemed like no time at all that they were joined by the young boy who emerged from a field ahead of them. The progress was slow. They would catch up now and then with groups of refugees, work their way through them, and plod slowly along the dirt road. Suddenly George stood up and waved his arms.

"Hey, those are my kids over there, come to meet us. We must be very close."

They were greeted by the rest of his family and Vita who was relieved no end to see George back, safe and sound. They quickly placed Eugenia's body in the pine box, nailed the lid shut and went to examine the truck.

The farmer shook his head. "What a mess! I don't know if it's worthwhile to haul it back, but we will take it. Might be able to fix it."

They harnessed the pair of mares and hooked them up to the bumper. The young boy would ride one of them, his father would ride in the cab, steering the truck and using the brakes, when necessary, while the grandfather would take the wagon with the body straight to the parish. Vita made a large pot of coffee, and they all sat down for a while. George wrote down his mother's name and dates necessary for a marker on her grave. He decided not to go back for the burial. He had done his duty. She was going into a proper cemetery, buried by a priest. He paid for a mass for her soul. This was the best he could do under the circumstances. He had to think of his family now, take them to a safe place, and try to figure out what to do next with their lives. He felt a heavy weight of responsibility on his shoulders. He looked at his youngest child. Jesus, he thought, what kind of future was there for him, only two years old. He gritted his teeth and clenched his fists. A wave of frustration and anger came over him. The German sons of bitches! They can't leave well enough alone; they never have enough; somebody ought to raze them off the face of this world. They don't deserve to live, every single one of them!

"Well, we better be going," he heard the farmer say. "Good luck on your journey, wherever you are headed."

They shook hands and the small, odd-looking group of people and machinery and the pine box slowly moved down the road. For a moment George wished he were going with them, back to the tranquility of the warm kitchen, supplies of food and good shelter; but then he thought of the approaching German troops, and he knew he had to get away from them as far as he possibly could. We've got to go east as far as we can, he kept repeating to himself, into the Puszcza.

They held a meeting in the grove over lunch and came up with a plan. They would take as many of their supplies and necessities as could be carried or loaded on the bicycle. The rest would be hidden in the grove under some heavy pine trees. If, by any chance, they found another, better means of transport, they could always come back to get them.

Vita had sewn some towels and work shirts together to form sacks and those were filled with tins of food and other supplies that were not too heavy, then the bundles were tied to the bikes. They wrapped the bedding together in blankets and fastened them to the bikes between the handlebars and the seat. Everyone able to do so would take turns pushing the bikes down the road. The smallest child could even sit on top of the bundles of the bike George was pushing. Vita and Ellie would take turns with the other bike. In addition to this, they each had bundles tied rucksack fashion on their backs. Vita's suitcase with the machine gun holes in it was strapped on top of the front fender, forming a wonderful shelf for a large sack with food supplies. The bikes looked grotesque, yet one person could easily push them. To carry the load would have been impossible.

They decided to wait till dusk, still fearful of the strafing planes; and when the sun went down, they left — a motley bunch with odd-looking "beasts of burden," making their way slowly in an easterly direction. They traveled in this fashion for three nights, resting during the day and finally they started noticing denser woods and boggy fields. The children picked the berries that grew abundantly around them. Their favorite was a type of red lingonberry, which also came in a black variety, evidently indigenous to that area. Nobody was familiar with that kind of berry, and they would have been careful not to eat them if it weren't for the fact that one of the smaller children ate a large quantity of them one day. Everybody panicked, wondering if the berries were poisonous, but the child was fine, so the suspicious black lingonberry became a part of their daily menu.

There was no doubt now that they were entering the famous Puszcza Bialowiejska. During their stops at scattered farms or villages to replenish their water and fresh produce, they would learn bits of news. The Germans were at their heels. Twenty miles back, the small town they passed was destroyed by fire; people were running away from there.

After all the available food was confiscated by the Germans on the neighboring farms, tanks would ride through destroying everything in their path. It was a nightmare! Dead horses and cows littered the roads everywhere. The German pilots strafed everything in sight! The farmer they were talking to was packing to leave. He had relatives on the Russian border and that's where he was going. But Warsaw was still holding on, he told them. Under constant shelling and bombing, against all odds, without food, water and electric power, the city was fighting off the enemy. At regular intervals Chopin's Polonaise could be heard over the loudspeakers.

****

8

POST NO. SEVEN

Between the dates of September 4th and 16th, the Polish Government,
the ministers, diplomats and the military high command
fled to Rumania, abandoning the country.
250,000 army men were simply left on their
own to fight as best they could.

September 11. George and his small group decided to make as many miles that night as they possibly could manage. The batteries in the bikes' lamps were miraculously holding up. They only used one at a time on the leading bike, the other following closely. That night they came upon a cluster of buildings that looked like farm buildings, but it couldn't have been that because they were located in dense woods with practically no open, tillable land in sight. The buildings were dark. There was no sign of life except a large, barking dog guarding the house. They shouted and shone their lights at the windows, but nothing happened. The dog wouldn't let them come near, so they decided to wait till dawn.

They settled down next to a shed, keeping a watchful eye on the big, growling animal. Ellie tried to talk to him sweetly, but to no avail. When morning finally came, they found that they were in a forester's yard. Right next to the gate there was a sign — GOVERNMENT FOREST PRESERVES — POST NO. 7. George explained that these posts were scattered all throughout the huge forests, all staffed with competent men in charge of the recreation areas, hunting licenses, game and wildlife. They were there to protect the game from poachers, patrol the area, and man the lookout towers watching for any signs of fire, etc.

"So," Vita said, "this house actually belongs to the Polish government?"

"Yes," said George. "Every forester has his own belongings, animals and so forth, but the buildings are all government property."

"Well then, if we were to stay here for the time being, we would not actually be taking over somebody's property, would we?"

"Well, no," answered George, "but I don't think we are deep enough into the woods as yet. You heard the farmer say the Germans are right behind us."

"That's true," Vita said, "but, on the other hand, how do we know whether we will be able to find another empty house in there, and also how do we know that the Germans won't go all the way to the Russian border? That little lane we took last night to this house would certainly not be adequate for tanks and troops. They would be more likely to travel down the main roads. I think we would be quite safe here. What do you think, Tania? Imagine sleeping in a bed again?"

Ellie was now concentrating on making friends with the large German shepherd. She got some meat out of a tin and placed it on the ground some distance from the dog, talking to him all the time. He was wagging his tail, but as soon as she made a move toward him, his ruff would stand up and he would bare his teeth. He was obviously hungry. He eyed the meat and the people around him frantically. It took Ellie an entire hour; the hunger finally won. The dog cautiously approached the meat and gobbled the food up in one huge swallow.

"Oh, that's a nice doggie," Ellie kept up a constant prattle. She finally got close enough to him to hand him a morsel and another and pretty soon she decided it was safe to pet him.

"He is a gentle old dog just doing his job," she announced.

Vita nervously watched the fast developing friendship between her young daughter and the ferocious-looking animal.

"Dear God, I hope he doesn't bite your hand off — he sure has large enough teeth!"

"Oh, Mother, he isn't going to do any such thing. I wish I knew his name."

They investigated the compound, peering into sheds and out-buildings. The larger one was a barn, its upper level filled all the way to the rafters with fresh-smelling hay. It obviously stabled horses in one portion. Some tack and parts of harness hung on pegs and on large beams.

"What happened to the animals?" Ellie wondered. "Look, Mother, this is where a cow was kept."

Straw lined the floor. There was a long feeding trough on one wall and a couple of milking buckets and a three-legged stool hung on pegs. Attached to the barn was a small chicken coop. The doors were wide open, the chickens gone.

"I will bet that when the forester decided to leave, he took what animals he could with him and let the rest out to forage for themselves," said George.

"But how about the dog? Surely he wouldn't leave an old dog behind," said Ellie.

It was a mystery all right.

When they finally got into the main house, all the signs pointed to a hasty, unplanned departure. Clothes were pulled out of closets, some dresser drawers were empty, some still full of linens and underwear. George found several guns stashed under the stairs leading up to the bedrooms. His eyes lit up.

"Look at this," he yelled. "Such beautiful shotguns and boxes of shells. I can now go hunting!"

In the spacious kitchen, dishes were still on the table, like somebody interrupted their meal, got up and left. There were two place settings and an enamel coffee pot half-filled with coffee. There was a loaf of bread on a breadboard, and a large knife beside it. Vita picked up the bread.

"It's quite dry. Must have been sitting here for a couple of days. Oh, I wish I knew what happened to these people."

George called from the next room. "Mrs. Kew, come over here."

He was in the forester's office. On the walls were several maps with multi-colored marks on them. The desk was messy with all kinds of papers stacked here and there. George was studying the large map on the wall.

"Look, here is where we are. This post is located between these two towns — Kobryn and Pinsk. Oh, I am afraid we are not far enough east — we will be caught here when the first Germans march into Kobryn. We have got to move on!"

"Now, wait a minute." Vita tried to calm him down. "Can't we stay here just for a day or two and see what happens? The Germans will not seek out every little house and murder every Pole they find in this whole country."

"Oh, no? You don't know them. They are all mad. I don't want to chance it!

You do whatever you want to — stay here, but we are leaving after we rest up a little and get some supplies together."

He was determined and Vita saw no point in arguing with him.

There were three bedrooms upstairs. They put the children in one. Vita and Ellie took the second, and George and his wife the last one. They all stretched out on the beds and luxuriated for a moment.

"Oh, this is heaven!" said Vita. "Haven't slept in a real bed for a long time."

"Look here, Mother, a bathtub!" shouted Ellie from downstairs. "We can take a real bath!"

They started a fire in the kitchen stove to prepare a meal. The water tank in the bathroom was also heated with wood — a very curious contraption. Vita and Ellie had never seen anything like it. The water was heated in a stove-like chamber by a furnace burning small chunks of birch wood. A large boxful of these chunks was located in the hallway between the kitchen and the bathroom. When the water was hot, the bather opened a separate spigot to fill the tub, adding cold water from a regular tub faucet and the bath was ready! Somewhere in the house there was a pump providing the water in the tank and into one square container, which hung high above the toilet. A long chain with a porcelain knob dangled from one side of the container. When the chain was pulled, the toilet flushed! All these modern facilities amazed the man.

"You would expect an outhouse here in the woods, but I guess when you're a government employee, nothing is too good for you!"

"What are you complaining about?" laughed Vita, "now YOU don't have to go to an outhouse!"

They spent the rest of the day discovering things about the house. There was a cool cellar where they found a large supply of food already put away for the winter. There were several smoked hams and sausages hanging from hooks; strings of dried mushrooms like garlands festooned the beams. There was a large barrel of sauerkraut and another of pickles and a crock of what looked like mushrooms in a brine, just like pickles! They were delicious! There were some preserves on the shelves, green beans, tomatoes and beets, and rows and rows of bottles with cherry, raspberry and blueberry syrup. There were jars with plum preserves and other fruit packed in jars enough to feed an army. They wondered why one small family would have so large a stock of food. Did the winters get so bad that they were completely cut off from the main road? But from the looks of the map, the town, with a railroad coming into it, was only ten kilometers away, an easy distance with a pair of horses and a sleigh. In the summer it would be an easy trip on a bicycle.

The bike! George had an idea. He would take a short trip down the road to some of the places marked on the forester's map. Those were probably other homesteads and maybe the people would still be there. He needed information. He had lost track of time. Was it the ninth or the tenth of September?

"Mrs. Kew, what's the date today?"

Vita consulted her calendar. "It's the eleventh."

"Jesus! It's terrible not knowing anything! There's no way to find out what is going on — no paper, no radio, nobody to talk to. I am lost! I think I will ride one of the bikes over to that point marked on the map. It's just a few kilometers. It could be another forestry, or a lookout tower, or a farm. Maybe someone still lives there."

They could not talk him out of it. Next morning, bright and early, he set out on his journey. He was gone well into the afternoon. The children ran down the road to look for him again and again, but there was no sign.

Ellie had walked quite a distance gathering berries and mushrooms when suddenly a crashing sound in the brush startled her and frightened her almost to death. She was about to drop everything and run away when she noticed with amazement a large black and white cow with a calf at her side. She came out of the brush and eyed her warily from a safe distance. Ellie noticed a chain and a tag on her neck.

Why, she must be the cow from the forestry, she thought. How do I get near her and bring her back. She took off her belt and very slowly moved toward the animal. The old cow was leery. She moved back with each step Ellie took forward. She doesn't trust me, the girl thought. Then an idea came to her. She picked up a handful of grass and stretched out her hand toward the young calf. It came right to her! She wrapped the belt around the calf's neck, leading it toward the path. The mother followed. Once in the barnyard, the cow was quite at home. She went immediately to the water trough to take a long drink, and the little calf followed her. Then they both marched into the barn and examined the grain bin. Here, for the first time, Tania became an authority.

"She will have to be milked. It was fortunate that she had this calf to suckle her or she would have had a terrible fever."

She took the three-legged stool, placed it expertly at the cow's side, and making sure Ellie held the cow's head at the trough, began milking her. A few squirts now and then hit the bucket, but the woman kept working away, squeezing and pulling each teat. Slowly the squirts became more even and finally about a pint gathered in the bottom of the large bucket.

"That's enough for now. We will have to do it twice a day, regularly."

"Mama, let me have some!" begged the small children.

"Now, wait. In a few days there will be plenty for everybody, but right now you can have just a little taste; the rest we have to save for the calf. And by the way, he is to be separated from the mother and fed some of the milk with a mash we will fix for him. He is too young to go on grass and grain only."

She was an expert on this subject. They all respectfully nodded agreement.

The children ran into the house for a small cup and everyone got a couple of swallows of the fresh milk.

"Yuk!" said Ellie when her turn came. She didn't like it at all. "It tastes terrible! Here, you have it." She handed the cup to one of the small children and wiped her mouth with her hand. "Terrible stuff, so thick and warm!"

They mixed the rest with some pulverized grain they found in a large bin and fed it to the calf. He either didn't like it, or didn't know how to drink it because all he did was sniff at it and bellow sadly. Tania again proved very knowledgeable. She poured the thick mash into a deep bowl, adding water to it, then she immersed her right hand into the bowl sticking two fingers out of it. She brought the fingers to the calf's mouth and got some of the liquid into it. Once he got the idea, he began sucking on her fingers, which she then lowered into the milk, making him reach for them. Slowly, slowly he began to slurp.

"Oh, let me do it, please?" asked Ellie.

"All right, here you go."

Ellie took the bowl over and followed the woman's instructions.

"I hope he doesn't bite my fingers off!" Ellie's eyes were as big as saucers.

"Oh, look at him. Isn't he cute? Look at the long eyelashes! And has he got an appetite!"

"After a while you can remove your fingers from the milk. He will get the idea," said Tania.

Ellie loved to feed him. This was to be her chore, twice a day. Also with the help of the other children, she was going to keep the straw clean in the two stalls for mother and baby.

"During the day," Tania said, "after the cow is milked, they can go out into the pasture to graze."

"Mrs. Dubczyk, would you please teach me how to milk, too?" Ellie begged.

"All right, tomorrow morning."

****

George finally returned, tired and discouraged. He had found a settlement a few kilometers away where several older people were still resolved to stay put, not really knowing what to do. Radio messages were conflicting at first, then after a few days, stopped coming. Somebody spread the rumor that the Polish government had fled the country — there were no leaders — everyone was on his own!

The only serious resistance the advancing German troops encountered was Warsaw. Almost totally destroyed, burning, without water, electricity and food, led by its mayor, Stefan Starzynski, the city hung on. Attack after attack was repelled at an enormous cost. Young and old fell by the hundreds under heavy shelling and bombing, but Chopin's Polonaise rang out at hourly intervals, played through the city's broadcasting systems, letting the world know that Warsaw was still alive, still fighting.

The most disturbing news, however, was the fact that all local jails were opened up and all the criminals let out. Anarchy raged. George found out from some of the people that the forester disappeared several days ago. He was the one who pleaded with the villagers not to panic, to wait for some direction...it was surely going to come. He rode from house to house trying to convince the people that nothing would be gained by running — it would just add to the confusion. He worked night and day, then he vanished! Some thought he gave up and left, others ventured a guess that when the jails opened he was murdered by criminals — he had put plenty of them behind bars. Some thought he was hiding in the woods. It was anybody's guess. They all advised George to move on...the bands of criminals roaming the countryside raiding houses were surely not going to spare him and his family. He was clearly frightened.

"Listen," he said to Vita, "if you want to stay, it's your business. I am not waiting here for some bandit to come and rape my wife or kill me or harm my children — and I think you are foolish if you stay. I know you want to get in touch with your family and you hope to find a working post office or some government agency that can help you, but don't you see — they are all gone. There is nobody to send that wire for you — there are no post offices, there are no consulates — you might as well forget it!"

A paralyzing feeling of fear crept to Vita's throat. For the first time since the insanity had started, she was really in a panic. The whole experience had been frightening, but this was different. The man was right. There was no way she could get in touch with anybody. She was helpless, at the mercy of either the Nazis or bands of criminals roaming the countryside. She had to protect herself and her child at all cost. But how? Was running further into the woods the answer, or trying to use her wits and intelligence to figure out a way to stay put and somehow protect themselves?

They decided to put the children to bed and resume their conference later. They sat in the dark office, the three of them, talking late into the night. They argued at length, but finally they came to an agreement. Vita won out. Tania agreed with her and together they swayed the man. They would stay! There was a roof over their heads; there was food, water and here they could sustain themselves for a long time. There were several shotguns available; George could provide some fresh meat. Not too far away there were fields of potatoes, beets and carrots — they could harvest those for winter. If the forester came back, fine — they were sure he would understand their predicament. In the meantime they would care for his possessions and his animals. The main thing was to stay out of sight of the wandering bands and, of course, the German Army.

They decided to spend the nights in the upper portion of the barn where the hay and straw were stored. With a lot of bedding, they would be comfortable. During the day they would keep watch, taking turns on the observation tower. One could see for miles from there. At first sight of anyone approaching, they would all hide in assigned places.

Considering the general exodus of the entire population, if anyone came to the house it would look deserted, just as it did when they arrived. The cow and calf would be out in the pasture away from the main house; the doors open to both the house and barn.

The children were to stay close to the house, always in sight of an adult. Lookout duty would be assigned to the three adults and Ellie, who was old enough and responsible. They would change every three or four hours.

So this was to be their plan. They also settled another important matter. All money, jewelry and papers had to be hidden somewhere in a safe place. Vita gathered them together and, ripping open the lining in her large leather bag, sewed all the items neatly in so that if the bag were turned inside out, they would be safe. Exhausted, but firm in their positive decision, they finally retired. The plan was to go into operation with the dawn.

For the entire next week they adhered to the routine pretty closely. From the tower they could observe the main road leading from Kobryn to Pinsk. The small dirt road leading to the forestry was extremely narrow and rutty. Through field glasses they could see groups of refugees traveling down the main road. They rode horse carts, cars and trucks, but mostly they walked. Vita felt sorry for them, but at the same time she felt relieved that she wasn't doing it. It was senseless in her opinion — senseless and stupid. She was to regret her decision, however, in a very short time.

****

Ellie was getting her milking lesson. Seated on a stool at the cow's side, a bucket between her knees, she carefully listened to Tania's instructions.

"Now, don't squeeze too hard, just enough pressure and a down-pull will bring the milk."

"There's nothing coming out!" Ellie was frustrated.

"Look." The woman reached over, grabbed one of the teats and with one movement sent a squirt of milk into the bucket.

"Oh, I see!" Ellie tried again. The cow swished her tail and the ends struck Ellie smack in the face.

"Hey, you kids, someone hold that tail!" she cried.

A pair of small hands reached up and grabbed the tail.

"Now," Ellie said and squeezed and gently pulled at the same time. A large squirt came out of the teat and went up her dangling sleeve.

"Don't aim into your sleeve! Aim into the bucket!" Tania slapped her thighs in merriment. Ellie tried again. Another squirt, straight into the other sleeve!

"Oh, for heaven's sake!" She tried to shake the milk out of her sleeves.

"You're doing just fine, just aim right!"

"Okay, I will try again."

This time she was very careful and nothing came out. The cow eyed her suspiciously.

"You sure she is not going to kick me?"

"Oh, I don't think so, but hurry up!"

Ellie tried again and again and finally all the motions fell into place and squirt after timid squirt, the milk began to cover the bottom of the bucket.

"I am doing it! I am doing it!" she cried.

"All right, now change over to the other two teats. You have to milk all four!"

She finally got the rhythm pretty well, with just an occasional squirt up her sleeve. She did a creditable job of filling about one-third of the bucket with warm, foamy milk.

"Mother, look! I did it all by myself."

Vita was amazed at her daughter. Here was a born farmer. Raised in large cities, she was drawn instinctively to the land and to animals, especially to horses; was eager to know all about agriculture, planting and harvesting, caring for animals and always wanting to live on a farm. Where on earth did this come from? Certainly not from her parents. Lord only knows, they tried. Eight fruitless years of piano lessons, three years of agonizing ballet, the best private schools, yet real happiness came from one-third of a bucket of fresh cow's milk!

It was strange, Vita thought. Ellie appeared to be in seventh heaven, on the surface at least. She would talk longingly about her father, recalling their adventures. She missed him and worried about whether they would be able to see him again soon, yet never once did she mention school or Mrs. Brandt and her piano lessons or any of the comforts of home. Vita came to the shocking realization that Ellie liked this kind of life. She was happy in the cow barn. She could sit by the hour observing the young calf, currying it and feeding it. Her hands and nails were grubby, her hair hastily braided into two long pigtails with pieces of straw sticking out of them, her boots, dusty and scuffed. She presented a dismal picture for a fourteen-year-old, well-bred young lady! Well, I'm certainly not going to worry about it now, Vita resolutely decided. In a way, this is better. I could not cope with a prissy — not the way we are living now. When we get back to normal, it will all change.

****

The days came and went with little change in the established routine. The lookouts saw nothing suspicious — same general movements of groups along the main roads leading east, few of them ever ventured into the deep woods toward the forester's house.

George finally relaxed and admitted to the women that they were probably right; it was wisest to stay put for awhile. The children were fine, looked healthy; everybody had more than enough food, all kinds of fresh vegetables and fruits.

They had fresh milk and cream, and this particular day, the biggest treat yet, freshly baked bread and real butter! The children watched Tania knead the dough, let it rise, then knead it again. When it finally went into the oven, she went into the cold storage room and brought out a crock of cream she had been collecting off the top of the milk which was stored there also. There was not a lot of it, but enough for a start. She poured the heavy cream into a wooden churn and, sitting down on a stool, placed the churn between her thighs and, hanging on to a broom-like handle, she raised it up and down in a rhythmical motion. At the end of the handle there was a round disc with holes in it. Sometimes tired of the up and down motion, she would place the handle between her open palms and roll it back and forth. The children, growing more and more impatient, offered to help, but she wouldn't hear of it.

"This one is all mine. Next time you can make a batch."

Finally she lifted the cover and, peering into the churn, she announced, "Almost ready!"

The children squealed with glee. A few minutes later she took the top off, removed the stick with the round disc, carefully scraping off all chunks of the yellow-gold butter from it and placing it into a large bowl of cold water. Then she poured off the buttermilk, catching all small particles, and then finally the largest chunks of butter. She then began working it with a small, flat, wooden spoon, washing out all the buttermilk, adding fresh cold water and forming a nice yellow ball. BUTTER!

It had been quite a long time since any of them had tasted fresh, homemade butter. Ellie never knew how butter was made — one went to the store and got it — but this was something quite wonderful, to be able to make it yourself!

That evening the two families sat down to a real treat. In addition to their regular meal, there was the best bread and butter they had ever had! George devoured a few slices with loud smacks and complimented his wife.

"This is good! You sure know your way around the kitchen!"

She smiled happily and said, "Let's thank the Lord. We owe it all to Him."

****

9

NIGHT OF TERROR

"They walked into the barn shining their flashlights at the wall and around the corner, looking for a shovel. They both stood two feet from the door, side by side. Vita squeezed Ellie with all her might. And then came the blast, rather two blasts so close together, they sounded like one."

Vita became more and more worried as she observed the fidgeting man seated across the table, nibbling on his supper. He had been more restless in the last few days — he would pace up and down in the room, deep in thought. She was trying desperately to think of something she could ask him to do. She already had him repair the pantry door. He had used up all the scraps of lumber in the barn, fixing fences and gates. He had sickled, by hand, a huge area of grass, dried it, turned it over with a pitchfork, then loaded it, bundle by bundle into a wheelbarrow and brought it into the barn which was already full of hay. It wasn't any good for fodder, but it could be used for bedding. He went hare hunting on several occasions, and bagged two. The man was only happy when he was busy — and he was running out of things to do.

One morning, Vita suggested that maybe it was safe to take another bike ride to the same house he had visited before, to find out the latest news, or maybe he could go to the main road and get information from the people still on the move. He thought that was a great idea!

"Now be careful," his wife admonished, as he wheeled down the road.

"Don't worry, I will be back soon."

He was back by mid-afternoon, and as he got off his bike, they all clustered around him, eager to listen. He was desperately trying to stay calm, but they could tell that what he was going to say wasn't going to be good news.

"We are safe from the Germans. They halted at a line running north and south some distance from here — but as of September 17, Russia has crossed the entire eastern Polish border and is occupying the whole eastern territory!"

The women were dumbfounded. "How can this be? Are they at war with Poland? Or with Germany?"

"No," replied George. "Apparently this is being done to give the Russians a 'buffer zone.' They have an agreement with the Germans, but they don't quite trust them, so as long as this area is available, why not take it? Of course, their explanation to the people is, 'We are here to protect you from the Germans and to establish order.'"

"We are done for!" he continued. "I don't know what to do anymore! How to get us out of this predicament. Some of the people I talked to say that thousands of Poles, some in uniform, some organized into makeshift army units, some just civilians like us, are pushing south towards Rumania. Apparently the border is open and they feel they can escape through there and get to France or England to join the Allies in the war."

Vita's eyes brightened at the prospect. "Listen, that's a wonderful idea! Why don't we go right away?"

"Do you know how far it is to the Rumanian border?" George exclaimed.

"No," replied Vita. "But we can soon find out!"

She ran into the house and pulled out a large map from the desk drawer and spread it over the kitchen table. The rest of them came in and gathered around it.

"Here is where we are at the present moment. So all we have to do is...." She stared at the map. "Oh, dear God, I didn't realize it was so far south of here."

"If we had some other means of transportation," mused George, "my truck, or a car, or something — maybe we could make it, but on foot, with small children and women, there is no chance — none at all!" He slumped into a chair. "We had best just stay here and take our chances with the Russians."

Vita was beside herself. Here was her opportunity to get into a neutral country. Surely in Rumania she could send a wire to Switzerland — they were not at war — the border was open — somebody might be able to help! She was close to tears. But George just shook his head in total dejection.

"There is no way. It is impossible! Hey, let's have something to eat! I am starving!"

The women automatically proceeded to put food on the table, but their attention was not on their work.

Vita was frantically thinking, trying to figure out a way to convince George to make an effort, to at least help him shake the feeling of dejection and to bring him back to his old fighting self.

"Listen," she started again after he had eaten some of his food. "What are the people like in the next post, the ones you visited? Have they got a car, a couple of horses?"

"Nah, they are old and the young ones took the transports, whatever there were when they fled. There is nothing around here that we could use. Don't you think I would jump at the opportunity if I thought we could manage to get away?"

He got up from his chair and before leaving the room, said: "We might as well move back into the house. There is no point in hiding in the barn at night. Once the Russians come in, I am sure there will be no bandits roaming around here anymore. It's martial law. The Russians won't put up with looting. I think we will be safe — at least from looters!"

It was too late to make the change-over that evening. They decided to spend the night in the barn again and then move back to the house next morning. Vita went about the usual activity as if in a daze — her mind in turmoil. She decided to take Ellie and either walk or bike over to the next post to see for herself. It wasn't that she didn't trust the man — she just did not want to give up when she felt there might be the slimmest chance of their getting out through Rumania. She had to try!

Except for the small children, sleep didn't come very easily that night. They all tossed and turned. It was a black night. It had been cloudy and rainy all afternoon and it looked like a storm was brewing. There was no moon, nor did any stars appear through the high barn window. Vita was about to ask George to go outside for a cigarette when, all three of them sat bolt upright and held their breaths...there was the sound of a motor of some kind laboring in high gear as if trying to get out of a rut in the road. Over and over it would whine in high pitch, then die down, then whine again, until finally it went silent.

George sprung up, grabbed his shotgun and positioned himself behind a partition high above the entrance to the barn.

"Everybody quiet and stay down!" he hissed. "Keep the children quiet!"

Now they heard the vicious barking of the dog.

"Oh, Jesus, the dog!"

The voices became louder. They were in the yard. The dog had evidently placed himself in the middle of the yard and defied them to come near.

"Get a flashlight," one voice said. "Can't see a damned thing."

They were not Russian soldiers. They spoke in the local Polish dialect, rough and full of profanities.

Now they could hear a car door being slammed and another voice from a distance: "Get that God-damned dog off my ass! There he is!"

There was a shattering blast — then total silence.

Ellie jumped to her feet, both hands pressed tightly to her mouth. Vita grabbed her around the knees and pulled her down. She reached for a blanket and tossed it over their heads. She held her in a vice-like grip. Tania had her hands full, trying to keep her three children quiet.

George, positioned just above the entrance door, was peering through a crack in the wall.

"There are only two of them," he whispered. "I can see them now. They turned on the light in the house. They are looking for something or somebody. One of them has a shotgun at the ready...now I don't want any noise out of any of you, understand?"

He climbed over some bales and lowered himself down to the rafters just above the barn entrance. Thus positioned, he aimed his shotgun straight down into the barn's passageway. It couldn't have been more than three feet away from the top of the opened door.

It seemed he stood this way for the longest time, motionless, like a statue. They all waited...afraid to breathe. Ellie brought her hand up to look at her watch. The illuminated dial showed 11:30.

"Suppose they stay overnight?" she whispered. "What then?"

"I don't know, love. We will think of something," Vita whispered back into the girl's ear.

"Here they come!" hissed George.

They all heard them approaching.

"Look in the barn. There must be a shovel in there somewhere!"

"Well, damn it, come with me and give me some light! I can't see anything!"

"The yellow son-of-a-bitch cleared out of here lock, stock and barrel — and just in time, too!" one of the men said.

"Yeah, the bastard!" the other replied.

They walked into the barn shining their flashlight at the wall and around the corner, looking for a shovel. They both stood two feet from the door, side by side. Vita squeezed Ellie with all her might. And then came the blast, rather two blasts so close together they sounded like one.

Tania screamed in unison with the wailing children. Ellie grabbed her mother in a death-grip and shook like a leaf.

"Oh God, did he kill them? she whispered. "Both of them?"

"I think so," replied Vita.

George jumped off the rafters and yelled, "Everybody stay up there. Don't move! Mrs. Kew, I need you down here. The rest of you stay up there and shut up!" He was at the end of his nerves, his voice broke.

"Oh, Mother, don't leave me here!" Ellie clung to Vita.

"It's all right, Ellie. I think it's all right. Here, move up to the others and try to keep them quiet. I will be okay."

She slid carefully down the familiar path between the straw bundles onto the platform, and then down a short ladder to the floor of the barn.

"Over here," George said. "First of all, let's make sure there were just two of them. Let's not turn on any lights yet. If there are more, the shots will bring them here and we don't want them to know who fired them."

It seemed they stood in complete silence for the longest time, occasionally peering out the door into the black barnyard and at the lighted house. There was no sign of life anywhere. Vita tried to keep her eyes averted from the two bodies sprawled a few feet away from where she was standing. Even though it was quite dark, she could almost sense what they would be like. A wave of fright and nausea swept over her. She could feel her whole body tense and rigid, pressing against the rough boards of the barn wall.

"Now listen," whispered George. "You stay here. I will go outside and make sure there is nobody else there. Now don't worry, I will be careful." He noticed her clenched hands held tightly to her face.

"What do I do if...?"

"Ssssh!" he silenced her, and with that, slipped out the door.

Vita's heart was pounding so hard she was sure it could be heard up in the loft.

"Mother, are you there? What's going on?" Ellie's whisper came down just above Vita's head.

"It's all right, Mr. Dubczyk went to check things out. As soon as he comes back, I think we will be safe. How are the others?"

"All right. Mrs. Dubczyk has them saying the Rosary!"

It seemed like another hour passed before George came back, finally talking in a normal voice. "There is no one else. The house is empty. There is some kind of small bus just outside the gate — looks like a school bus. I haven't taken time to look it over.

We will do it when it is light. Right now, will you and Ellie please hand me some blankets from the loft? We will cover the bodies up for now, the dog too, so we can take the children out of here and move them to the house. It's safe. Go through the cowshed in the back and use the other door. Ellie, help with the kids."

"Yes, Mr. Dubczyk," replied Ellie obediently.

They got them all down. George carried two of the smaller children, his wife led the oldest by the hand. They followed Ellie holding the flashlight and went out through the back door. George slid the barn door shut and he and Vita followed the group into the main house. The place was chilly. They closed the doors, turned out all the lights and huddled in the kitchen where Vita started a fire in the stove. They were all very quiet. The youngest child was in his mother's lap, rocking gently...his eyes closed, thumb in his mouth.

Well, there's no use sitting around here. Let's get some sleep, if we can. Tomorrow we will need our strength," said George.

"Do you think we should keep watch?" asked Vita.

"Well, suit yourself," he said. "I, for one, am going to bed!"

He helped get the children upstairs and they all settled in their bedrooms.

Vita put a few more logs on the fire and she and Ellie sat on the large bench. It was 2:30 a.m.

"What will we do now?" asked Ellie.

"I wish I knew!" sighed Vita.

"Do you know who the two men were? Could you see what they looked like? Suppose they were bandits?"

"Ellie, you know it was pitch black there...and as far as knowing who they were...you heard them — they were after the forester and who knows what they would have done to us if they had found us in the barn. Mr. Dubczyk saved our lives most certainly. He had to do it. If he weren't around, I would have done it myself!"

"Oh, me too! Me too!" echoed Ellie. "What will you do with the bodies?"

"Oh, please — Mr. Dubczyk probably has a plan. We will know tomorrow morning. Aren't you tired?"

"Oh, no. I couldn't sleep for anything, right now. Please, Mother, let's just sit here by the fire. If you want, you can stretch out on the bench. I will get you a pillow and a blanket."

They settled themselves close together, staring at the flickering flames. Vita's thoughts were a shambles. She tried to put aside the happenings of the night and think only of tomorrow. Now there was some kind of bus available to them. Now they could go to Rumania. Would George agree? After all, they couldn't stay here any longer. What if those two in the barn were not who they thought they were, bandits and looters? What if somebody came looking for them? No, they couldn't take that chance. George would see the light. They had to get out of this house and this area. This time, Vita thought, Fate was playing into her hand. If they got out of here, they would certainly not go any further east — the Russians were occupying the country. Surely, George wouldn't insist on going any closer towards them than they already were. The other alternative would be to go south. They could travel on secondary roads, slowly making their way toward the Rumanian border. Oh, dear God, she thought, I hope we can do it!

Off and on she would hear footsteps upstairs. He wasn't sleeping either, just pacing up there, thinking. Finally, he came down. Ellie had curled up in one corner of the bench and was fast asleep. Vita carefully got up and quietly followed him into the office. It was almost dawn.

They sat down at the desk and, in a voice reduced to a whisper, George said, "Now, as soon as we can see outside, you and I are going out there to take care of the bodies. I have been thinking. There is an abandoned well behind the shed. You know, the one with the cover on it. We can drag them over there and dump them into it. It would save us a lot of time. Otherwise we would have to dig a grave and we won't have time for that!"

"Oh, you are so right," whispered Vita, "no time at all!"

She didn't know what he meant, but decided to agree with him in anything he said.

"Now, I have told Tania to keep the children, including Ellie, in the house until we are through. She is awake. We didn't sleep at all up there. I wish I had some coffee!"

Vita went to the stove and brewed up two large cups of strong coffee. They drank it in silence and then she slipped upstairs to change her clothes. When she came down, George was arguing with Ellie.

"I can help, too. I don't understand why you always treat me like a baby,..I am not, you know. I am fourteen years old, and I am strong!"

"I know, Ellie, but this time, just for a while, please trust me. We will call you as soon as the bodies are taken care of, all right?" said George.

"Ellie," Vita jumped in, "Mr. Dubczyk knows what he is doing. Please listen to him."

"Okay, okay, but when you go to look at the bus, I want to go too!"

"Sure, sure, you can — we promise!"

They stepped out of the house. Dawn was just breaking. They could see pretty well around the barnyard. The first thing they noticed was a mound in the middle of the yard, covered with a blanket. George slid one side of the blanket under the animal and, grabbing all four corners, dragged it towards the well. Vita ran ahead of him and slid the partially deteriorated cover off the top. The sides of the well were built out of bricks and had been taken down or had fallen apart, because now they were only two feet high. The roof above it still stood with an old frayed rope wound around the beam. He easily swung the bundle over the side and they could hear the thud as the animal landed at the bottom.

"It's dry," he said, "and quite deep."

They now skirted the barn and entered it from the back, the way they had left it the night before, without opening the front door. George went to the opposite side of the barn and handed Vita a rake.

"Please, go out there and rake some dirt over the blood spot where the dog lay."

"All right," said Vita, eagerly.

She found the spot and, scraping the gravel and dirt, covered it up. There was surprisingly little for such a large dog, she thought.

When she got back, George had slid the front door partially open and was examining the bodies.

"Jesus Christ," he said when she came close. "Look at this!"

It took all of her willpower to direct her glance in that direction. The two bodies sprawled on the floor wore army uniform coats. Muddy boots stuck out from under them. The insignia on the epaulettes looked like officers' but it was hard to see because they were covered with blood. There was blood everywhere, splattered on the walls, the door, all over their bodies and jelled into dark puddles around them on the floor. She gagged repeatedly.

"Now, now, Mrs. Kew," said George, "don't go fainting on me. I need your help. remember, we've got to do it!"

"I'll be all right," she replied, fighting tears and nausea with all her strength.

George turned one of the bodies face up. "Face" was not the right word, because there was no face. It was one bloody mass. He slipped a corner of the blanket over it, covering the most gruesome sight, and proceeded to unbutton the coat.

"Oh, for Heaven's sake," whispered Vita, "let's get them out of here!"

"No, I want to know...."

He did not finish because under the coat he found no uniform, but a dirty brown shirt and black pants stuffed into high riding boots. Next to the body, partially under it, lay a gun. He picked it up and examined it carefully.

"It's an army carbine, regular issue. I know them. Now, where did they get these coats, boots and the gun?"

"I really don't know, Mr. Dubczyk, but what difference does it make?" whined Vita. "Let's do what we have to do!"

"Oh, but it makes a great big difference to me, Mrs. Kew. I am the one who killed them. I feel much better now that I know they were up to no good!"

He was now going through the coat pockets and came up with a handful of money. Neither of them had a wallet, nor any identification.

"I'll bet they are local riff-raff, fresh out of jail," he said.

"Oh, I knew that all the time. Didn't you hear their language and the way they referred to the forester? They were after him, and they would have killed him had they found him."

"You bet they would have," replied George. He now took a length of rope from a peg on the wall and began tying the blanket around the first body. "We will need another one."

She reached over and handed him a pair of long, leather reins. He tied them around the middle and, handing Vita one end, grabbed the other and they both slid the body over the stoop and out the door. They dragged it around the corner of the barn, behind the shed and dumped it into the well. They did the same with the other. George cleaned up the carbine and set it aside. Then they proceeded to clean up the rest. Vita suggested they cover the floor with the freshly cut hay George had just brought in. They spread a thick layer all over the floor and stomped it down with their feet. They decided to ignore the walls. They collected all the rest of the bedding still up in the loft. George picked up several of the guns he had hidden in the barn and as they slid the barn door shut, their grisly work done, the sun was just over the horizon.

In the kitchen, Ellie and Tania had fixed breakfast. Ellie was full of questions.

"Not now. I will tell you all about it later, O.K.?" said Vita.

They took turns washing up and came back to have some coffee.

"How about the car?" said Ellie.

"That's the next thing," replied Vita.

"Now, you promised to let me look." Ellie was pestering them, no end.

"Sure, we will all go and see."

"Ellie, have you forgotten? It's milking time!" Tania reminded her.

"Oh, Mrs. Dubczyk, will you do it for me this morning? Just this morning?"

"You may not have another chance," George said.

Vita's heart skipped a beat. He is planning to go, she thought.

"What do you mean, no other chance?" the girl wanted to know.

"Well, here is our opportunity. We now have a car. After we check it out, and if it is okay, we might as well try our luck in getting out of here."

"Oh, that's great!" exclaimed Vita. "That's wonderful!"

"You will see. We will make it through the border and we will be safe in Rumania!"

"I hope so," came the reply.

Tania and her oldest daughter went to bring the cow and calf from the pasture for milking. The rest of them went to the gate where, behind the lilac rows, sat a black, square, curious-looking vehicle.

"That's not a school bus!" said Vita.

"Well, in the dark I couldn't make out what it was," he replied.

"Look here, there are bars on the door windows. It's a wagon from the prison."

They all circled around it a couple of times, dumbfounded. George opened the door and got into the driver's seat. A foot behind the two front seats was a partition separating this part of the wagon from the rest with a heavy gauge wire mesh. Behind it, on either side, were two large benches, facing each other. The two windows on either side had bars on them, also. The back of the wagon was incredible. It was loaded, almost to the top, with bedding, clothes, food supplies, guns, ammunition, and at the very end, there was a large box, full of grenades!

George let a long whistle escape his lips. "Oh, brother! Have you ever seen anything like it?"

Along one side there was a row of cans about two feet high, olive green, like army issue. George opened the top of one and exclaimed, "Gasoline!"

Everyone cheered.

Ellie was outside examining the rut the wagon was stuck in.

"It's just the one rear wheel. We can easily fill the hole with dirt, or lay a board in there," she was shouting.

"Wait a minute." They could hear George swearing. "Psia Krew!" Cholera!

"What's the matter?" Vita was right beside him in the passenger seat.

"There are no keys in the ignition!"

"Oh, my God! Do you suppose they were...?"

"Well, where else could they be? I suppose one of the bastards had them in his pocket!"

"But, you looked in the pockets!"

"Not all of them!"

Ellie, standing on the running board at George's elbow, said, "You can jump the wires, that's no big thing. I remember one time Daddy and I lost the keys to the Austin at that hill climb he was in. He pulled two wires from under there, cut them, and then, by crossing them, started the engine. It worked great. The only thing, we couldn't stop the car until we got home!"

"Well, that's easy for you to say. I'm no mechanic. I don't know anything about wires. What two wires?"

"I really don't know." Ellie was not quite ready to give up. "The ignition wires, I suppose!"

"Ignition wires!"

"Oh, Papa, Papa, the keys are here!"

The oldest boy was pointing at the back door. Sure enough, the key ring with several keys dangling from it was in the lock of the door.

Oh, thank God, thought Vita. Any more of these shocks and my heart will give out.

They handed the keys to the man and he turned on the engine. Putting it in gear, he tried to move forward or backward, but the wheel was so imbedded it would just spin in the dirt.

"Well, Ellie is right, a large board or some gravel in there and we can get it out easily."

He went back to the house and brought out several pieces of wood, filled the hole with them and then propped a board from under the tire across the whole rut.

"Now, Ellie, you get in there, put it into second gear, and slowly, and I mean slowly, roll forward. All the rest of us will give it a push!"

It took several tries, but finally the wagon's tire took a grip on the board and rolled over it and on to the road.

"Okay, okay, now drive it up to the front of the house. We will have to unload most of this stuff, hide the artillery, and load it up with supplies and I really think we should try to get out of this place by nightfall."

"We all agree to that," shouted Vita. "Let's get to work right now!"

"What will happen to the cow and the calf?" Ellie was upset at the idea of abandoning the animals.

"Well," George scratched his head, "we will have to leave them in the field — the one with the stream in it."

"Now, wait a minute." Vita had an idea. "Those old people you went to see the other day, they don't live too far away. Couldn't we stop and tell them to come by and fetch the animals?"

"I suppose we could."

"They might be glad to have a cow and a calf."

"Yeah, that's a good idea. It's right on our way anyway. We will just stop by and tell them to get here in the morning and take the animals and whatever else they might need for themselves. They have a neighbor with a horse and a wagon. He will give them a hand, I'm sure."

They now proceeded to unload the wagon of all the stuff the two men had amassed. It was unbelievable! When finally the back of the wagon was emptied, they realized how big and roomy it was.

"We must take all the gasoline we can," George declared. "We can place the cans under the benches. Let's tie them securely under there so they will not move around."

They also noticed that the heavy-gauge metal partition between the driving cab and the main van had a door in it with a large padlock hanging in the hasp.

"It would be nice to have this open," thought George, aloud.

Ellie raised her finger up. "Just a minute. I think I might help you there!"

She brought the key ring from the cab and tried the keys, one by one.

"Aha! Here it is! Great!"

The door swung open and they padlocked it to the wire in the open position. Now they could all move freely between the cab and the van part of the wagon.

They worked feverishly all day with only a short break for lunch. When dinner time approached, they were almost ready. Maps, two guns, ammunition, clothing, bedding, loads of food, containers of water, money, a pair of binoculars and a box full of looted jewelry they had found in the wagon, which Vita scooped into her voluminous handbag, saying: "This is better than money!"

The van began to look as bad as when they first started unloading it. The whole back area was reserved for a sleeping section. They placed a couple of mattresses on the floor with plenty of bedding on top. The sitting section had a row of boxes and suitcases in the middle of the aisle. The two long seats would accommodate six sitting people, or two sleeping, so there was ample space for the seven passengers, both for traveling and sleeping. They took a small, one-burner primus, some pots and pans, and finally, George put a halt to it.

"Now, wait a minute — that's enough! It will not take us all this long to travel down to the border. For Heaven's sake, we are so loaded down the engine won't pull us up a hill!"

"Supper is ready," called Tania.

She had baked a whole, smoked ham. They could take it along and have meat for a couple of days. After finishing the huge meal, they closed up the house, did their chores and, at dusk, climbed aboard the wagon and slowly were on their way.

Ellie looked back several times with tear-filled eyes.

****

10

ON THE ROAD AGAIN

*On September 17, 1939, the Soviet Union invaded
Eastern Poland occupying any territory not already seized
by the Germans, according to the Nazi-Soviet Treaty
signed the previous month. Stalin declared that he was acting
"to restore peace and order in Poland, which has been destroyed
by the disintegration of the Polish state."*

The large jail van made slow progress on the dirt roads, staying away from main highways. Traveling at night seemed most safe but also very tedious and slow. Some of the roads were not marked, most of them not recorded on even the most accurate maps George had taken from the forestry. When the woods became denser, it was impossible to recognize anything during the dark nights, so some days they traveled in the very early hours.

The woods were magnificent! Large, ancient, tall trees, dense underbrush, meandering paths lined with ferns, berry bushes and an abundance of mushrooms. The children gathered them, and Tania identified them expertly and then prepared them for their meals. George bagged a hare and a couple of pheasants for a special feast.

Ostensibly, they were a happy group on an outing, living with nature in a wilderness far away from war, seemingly carefree and at peace. Inwardly, each one of them fought a private war. Vita, anxious and impatient to get to the border and into the safety of a neutral country; George, uncertain, apprehensive of what the future held for him and his family in a strange country. He was a farmer with no special skills — what would he do there to support all of them? He was much more at home right here in the woods, but then he thought of the Germans to the west and the Russians to the east and fear gripped him. The Swiss lady was determined to go over the border; she never wavered from her original plan to get herself and her daughter out of Poland and back home. It made sense for her. He understood that. But he? What should he do? He was moody, short-tempered and indecisive.

They worked their way south, through the middle of the "jungle." They noticed that the ground became boggy in some areas and the vegetation took on a different look. As the map indicated, they were approaching the wide, marshy area of the Puszcza Bialowiejska. Traveling would become much harder and slower. George was worried.

"You know," he would say, "some of these parts of the country are so marshy nobody can get through. What the hell will we do then?"

"Can't we go around them?" asked Vita.

"Jesus, to go around the bogs will put us back in the arms of the Germans! No, we can't go back there. We have to work our way south, somehow. The map shows that these bogs extend east all the way to the Russian border, so we can't circle them that way."

He felt trapped and helpless.

They camped one day in a small meadow, the children gathering lingonberries which grew in clumps on small islands among the boggy, soggy channels. They hopped from one small island to another, picked the berries and moved on. Their squeals of laughter could be heard for miles in the still forest. George, annoyed at the noise, stormed out of the van and marched angrily to the edge of the meadow to call the children back. As he turned, he found himself staring into a double-barreled shotgun. He froze. The man holding the gun was tall and strong.

"Who are you and what are you doing here?" he asked.

"Oh, shit, did you scare me!" exclaimed George. He grinned nervously and proceeded to introduce himself and tell the stranger why he was there. The tall man eyed him suspiciously, then he heard the children merrily returning from the bog, their containers filled with berries, red-stained hands and faces.

He relaxed, put his gun down and greeted them. George motioned to him to follow, and they all went in the direction of the van where the two women were preparing a meal. When he spotted the jail van, his eyes widened.

"Where the hell did you get that?"

"Oh, ah, we found it — it was abandoned. We are trying to drive down to the Rumanian border."

"Through this?" asked the man, pointing to the bogs.

"Well, yeah, what else can we do?" George replied.

The man just shook his head. He suggested they all come to his house. George gladly agreed. Vita, too, was anxious to find out all she could about the feasibility of her plan.

****

11

A PEACEFUL SOJOURN

*"Finally, on September 27th, with 12,000 citizens dead,
one-quarter of the city destroyed and much of the rest in flames,
with food stocks gone, the water system wrecked, Warsaw gave in.
The Chopin had died away; the radio station had gone off the air.
And there descended on Poland a great curtain of silence."*

Otto Friedrich
TIME Magazine

The small white cottage was nestled under huge trees at the end of a long, narrow path. Ivan Nadvorny, an eccentric, had taken residence with his wife, Tekla, and his son, Greg, in this remote part of the forest in order to write in solitude.

He explained the guests to his wife who smiled broadly and said, "So that's where the noise was coming from. We couldn't imagine who was out there!"

She laid the table in the kitchen with all such wonderful things as freshly-baked bread, homemade butter, sausage, cheese and cups of hot chocolate and coffee. The children enjoyed the meal immensely. They had never yet gone hungry, but this was a feast!

After the meal was over, the writer told them that German troops had halted at the Curzon Line in agreement with Russia, which then proceeded to occupy Eastern Poland up to that line. Order and police power were restored by the Russian Army, which now was taking a census of the population. People were asked to register at local government offices in the villages and towns. Russia was going to take care of that part of Poland; help the people go back to more or less normal lives again, fill the missing official posts, open schools, set up temporary government offices and restore law and order. The occupation was to be regarded as a friendly, helpful gesture of a neighboring country for an indefinite period of time.

Germany's invasion of Poland was halted which, by itself, was a blessing. No more destruction, no more bloodshed. The war in Poland was, for all practical purposes, over, save for persistent, clandestine activities of some remnants of the Polish forces, now underground. News somehow trickled through about a German munitions transport blowing up, a bridge collapsing sending a German convoy into the river, snipers ambushing German patrols. Such news was always received with great joy and pride. George clenched both his fists in a triumphant gesture of approval.

"It does my heart good to hear this. We haven't all given up! The spirit of Poland still lives!" he exclaimed, obviously moved.

Ivan discouraged the group from further travel. He felt they were safe where they were. If the Russians meant what they said, Vita and Ellie could soon go back home. George and his family could settle temporarily in some abandoned house, of which there were many, and wait out the war. He was not quite convinced about all the good intentions of the Soviet Government. But as long as they were saying that the occupation was only temporary and when the war was over they would return the land to the Poles, he was willing to give them the benefit of the doubt. Russians were not welcome in this area, but they now had an upper hand and most of the Poles were willing to temporarily forget their deep-seated hatred and assume a "wait and see" attitude.

After many arguments and persuasions, George and Vita accepted Nadvorny's hospitality and decided to stay. George and his family were given two upstairs bedrooms and Vita and Ellie were put on the main floor in a small den, converted into a bed-sitter with a large, sunny window and a pot-bellied iron stove in one corner. Ellie immediately made friends with a brace of large, wire-haired dachshunds, three or four of them who were all over the house.

George was in seventh heaven having another man to hunt with and to help with the chores around the small, farm-like outpost. There were chickens, an old horse and a small pig in a pen. All of this represented stability once more — a home-like atmosphere which gave everybody a good feeling of security.

Vita paid Ivan and his wife a sum of money for their hospitality. They accepted it gratefully; there were many things they would be needing when normalcy returned to their lives. They planned a trip to town to replenish their supplies before winter set in.

"Winters over here are pretty rough," said Ivan. "Sometimes we are cut off from the main road for weeks. This year, however, the weather has been so nice that maybe winter will be mild and short. Let's hope so."

****

October, 1939. Life settled down to daily routine in a very short time, the children romping in the woods, fishing in the well-stocked pond, gathering mushrooms and berries. Tekla dried mushrooms for the winter. There were strings of them hanging from the rafters in the kitchen over the large brick stove where the fire never died; it was rekindled every morning and fed all day. There were wondrous things cooked on that stove and baked in the large brick oven. She was an excellent cook. Her pantry was lined with shelves from floor to ceiling each jammed with jars of vegetables and fruit and meats, all put up for winter.

Vita wrote in her diary. She had kept it daily from the very beginning of this insanity. By now it filled quite a number of pages in the small, leather-bound calendar. There were many comments on almost every aspect of their ordeal. She hoped to read these to Paul one day. She could almost see his shocked and horrified expression when she and Ellie recounted all their experiences. It shouldn't be too long now. As soon as order was re-established in the country, she would be able to make arrangements to go back home. Home — what a sweet word!

Her eyes filled with tears. She quickly got up, put her writing things away, and went to the kitchen to give Mrs. Nadvorny a hand.

November was unseasonably warm. By this time, snow should have covered the ground. This part of Poland had very severe winters lasting approximately four months, November through February, with lots of snow, cold temperatures, a couple of hard winter storms. This year, the weather was very mild. The children spent most of the days outside. Young Greg was in charge of wood preparation for the two fireplaces as well as the kitchen stove. He got Ellie and George's children to give him a hand and all of them carried the split wood into a large shed and stacked huge mounds clear to the rafters. Ivan and George either hunted or fished.

The days passed quickly, and Vita became quite impatient that nothing was being done to prepare for her departure. The men went into the small town on several occasions but always came back with conflicting, strange stories. Hitler was being attacked from all sides. The war should not last too much longer. On the other hand, the Russian occupation was in full operation. All government officials, police force, teachers, and so on, were now Russians. The Poles were mysteriously being removed. The speculation was that they were being transplanted to different territories. Some people suspected, but did not know for certain, that they were being shipped into Russia to make room for Russian families who were being settled all throughout the occupied zone. People were frightened, uncertain of the future, wondering when their turn would come if, indeed, they, too, were to be taken. Nobody understood why such mass evacuation was taking place. It didn't make sense to move all the people out of one country and into another. It was inconceivable that such a plan would even work. How would they feed them all — what would they do with them?

Vita and the other adults at the house would sit up late into the night talking about all this. It was sheer nonsense. Ivan Nadvorny registered at the Town Hall. He felt that perhaps the Russians would leave him and his family alone if he followed orders. George wouldn't think of doing any such thing.

"I don't trust the S.O.B.'s," he said, "besides, I am not from these parts, so they won't even know I am living here. No, sir, I am not putting my name on any list!"

During the first days of December the snow started to come. It snowed enough to cover the ground sufficiently to get the sleds out of the storage shed, and the children spent long days outside having a good time. Greg and Ellie, who were the same age, would run off with their toboggan before the younger children could be bundled up, and, free from them, they would venture to the steepest hill they could find and slide down at reckless speeds. They would come home, exhausted, red-cheeked and ravenous. Winter was wonderful!

On December 20th, Ivan gathered all the children together and announced that they would all go to the woods to find a Christmas tree. The children were overjoyed. They followed him through the barnyard and down the path leading to the forest. Everywhere they looked, there were Christmas trees — small ones, medium sized and huge!

The children would point one out and yell, "Here, here! I found the best one!"

"No, no, mine is much nicer!"

"You dummy, you can't put this tree into a room! It's twenty feet high!"

"It is not! It only looks like it out here!"

"Mr. Nadvorny, look here. Can't we cut this one? I found it all by myself!"

Ivan circled the tree, giving it a scrutinizing look, then stood next to it to see how much taller the tree was.

"Well, it looks pretty good, but I think we can find an even better one."

So the group wandered off to a clump of smaller, thicker pines, and, after much arguing and measuring, they finally chose a lovely spruce and Ivan cut it down. He then tied a rope to the stump and they all took turns pulling the tree home.

The rest of the day was spent placing it in the large family-sitting room and decorating it with hundreds of Christmas decorations which Mrs. Nadvorny brought down from the attic. Real, red candles in their small silver holders were snapped to the branches. These would be lighted only on Christmas Eve and Christmas day. For the present, the tree, decorated and ready, would stand there for the few preceding days, behind closed doors, waiting for Christmas Eve.

There were very few things under the tree, but everybody got some little thing or other made by Vita or liberated by George during his trips to the bombed-out towns. There was a large flashlight for Ivan, a pretty wool scarf for his wife, mittens and hats, made by Vita, for all the children. There was no Christmas paper, so all the gifts were wrapped in old newspaper and the children drew colorful designs with crayons and pasted decorations on the packages. Christmas was going to be grand in spite of the war and the desperate situation. It was going to be joyous and gay and festive.

Vita and Ellie, saddened by their missing husband and father, put on a valiant effort to join in the preparations. Each one tried to hide her feelings from the other.

"There is nothing we can do about this right now," Vita said, "but we shall make it up next year. When we are back home again, we shall have the happiest and best Christmas ever!"

The ladies were now baking cookies and making candy and distributing the goodies onto ten colorful plates, one for each person. They were almost heaped high. A tag with each person's name perched on top. There was a feeling of excitement and anticipation in the air — soon, soon. The children were counting the days.

****

In the early hours of December 24th, around 1:30 a.m., there was a loud pounding on the front door. Ivan Nadvorny slipped into his pants and jacket and, grabbing his gun, went cautiously downstairs.

"Who is it?" he asked.

"Open up!" commanded a man's voice in Russian. "This is the Soviet Army!"

Nadvorny cracked open the door to see three uniformed figures standing on the stoop.

What happened next was beyond belief as Vita later described it in her diary. Through the closed door of the little den, which she and Ellie occupied, she could hear the commotion...the angry voices of Ivan and the strangers and then Tekla, now weeping, now arguing. They were ordered to show their papers and then given only a few minutes to get dressed. The man evidently in charge was mean and impatient.

"Hurry up!" he yelled. "We don't have all night!"

Then young Greg's voice could be heard, angry and defiant, "What is this? Are you arresting us? For what?"

He was silenced with a loud slap. Vita could hear the scuffle that ensued, angry voices and orders. She could sense in the dark that Ellie was getting on her clothes.

"Mother, what's going on?" she whispered.

"Be very quiet," said Vita in a low tone. "Have you got your clothes on? Okay, open the window."

"What?" Ellie was stupefied.

"Just do it! Now get out as quietly as you can!"

"How about you?" whispered Ellie.

"Go! I'll be right behind you!"

She wrapped a blanket around herself and, grabbing her purse, slid out the open window. They both struggled to pull the window shut behind them and huddled under it. It seemed forever. It was a very cold night and it snowed heavily. Later she remembered thinking, "This is Christmas Eve!"

Ellie was sniveling. "They are taking the Nadvornys and Greg, aren't they?"

"Yes," whispered Vita.

"And how about Mr. Dubczyk?" Ellie was now weeping helplessly.

"I don't know, and please stop crying. I...." She was interrupted by the sound of a slamming door and voices saying something she could not understand. Presently an engine was started, revving loudly and unevenly, and finally they could hear the machine move slowly down the driveway...then total silence.

The snow was falling in big heavy flakes, sticking to everything. Ellie brushed it off her face and, lifting herself up, tried to peer into the window.

"I can't see anything in here. How long will we sit here? Mother, aren't you cold? You aren't even dressed!"

"Ellie, go around the house and see if they are gone."

Ellie moved in a low crouch between the building and some bushes and rounded the corner.

"There is nobody there. I think it's safe to go in."

As they made their way to the door, George Dubczyk and Tania appeared. "Mrs. Kew, where have you been? I've been looking all over for you. I didn't see you on the truck."

"Oh, thank God they didn't take you too," said Vita. "Where were you?"

"We went up to the attic...see that little window up there?"

"Mr. Dubczyk, let's get inside. I am in my slippers and my feet are numb!"

"Oh, my God, you must be frozen!" Tania exclaimed.

"Well, I've been warmer!" said Vita.

It was now 3:00 a.m. They all huddled around the kitchen stove, stunned and unbelieving.

"What did I tell you?" Dubczyk finally spoke up. "Don't put your name on any stupid list, but does anybody ever listen to me? No, Ivan had to go and register! Look what it got him! The Russians are our enemy, always have been. You can't trust the S.O.B.'s!" He was in such a rage that Tania motioned to Vita to keep quiet.

Vita took the hint and, lifting her coffee mug, said "Merry Christmas to us all!"

****

Christmas Day. There was nothing anybody could say or do to persuade the man that his decision to leave was not very wise.

"I am not staying here another day. Mark my words. They will be back."

"Why would they come back?" Vita implored. "They don't know we are here. Besides, what makes you think you can travel in that van without being spotted?"

"I will take my chances. It's better than sitting here waiting for them to get me!"

"George," Tania begged, "there is a blizzard out there. The roads are bad. Couldn't we at least wait for the weather to settle down?"

"No, the roads are frozen now, and the snow is not all that deep. We have a much better chance to make it now. Once spring thaws come, it's too late."

Vita was torn. Her instincts told her to stay, but her heart ached at the thought of letting them go, the only friends she now had, but she must use her head. Here was shelter and food; out there, the unknown. No, she reasoned with herself, I can't take that chance.

George was packing up provisions and clothing, urging the rest of his family to stop moping and get ready.

"Mrs. Kew, I hope to God you will change your mind and come with us. I would hate to leave you here alone."

"We will be just fine," she replied. "You might be back in a couple of days when you get stuck in a snow bank." She was sad to let them go but convinced that her choice was the most sensible.

****

January, 1940. Those were desperate days. Christmas and New Year's came and went without any change in the monotonous routine of everyday existence. The solitude was the worst. There was nothing to do except to keep the fires going, take care of the animals, prepare meals and wait. Wait for what? Vita, in her many sleepless nights, agonized over her decision to stay behind. Maybe she was wrong.

What if, what if.... But one couldn't live by "ifs." She was worried about Ellie. The girl was so thin and pale. She lost her appetite, became listless — she didn't even argue anymore.

"We should have gone with them," was the only comment she made.

There was one fortunate thing. Ellie loved to read, and the Nadvorny's collection of books was immense. She would stretch out on her bed, surrounded by two or three dogs and lose herself in a story for days at a time.

Vita wrote letters — to Paul, to friends, to anybody. She filled long pages with her adventures, thoughts, hopes and despairs. And so the time dragged on.

****

One bright and sunny morning, Vita bundled Ellie up and sent her out to play with the dogs. And then she heard the bells. Now I am really losing my mind, she thought, shaking her head. But the sound persisted and seemed to be coming closer and closer. She ran outside to call Ellie when a horse and a sleigh appeared in the driveway. Two people in fur coats and hats waved a greeting.

"Hello there," a man said, "is Ivan home?"

Vita walked up to the sleigh.

"Oh, I am sorry, Ivan and his family were taken by the Russians Christmas Eve. My daughter and I are the only ones here. You have no idea how glad I am to see you! Please come in. Oh, here is my daughter now."

Ellie ran up to them surrounded by barking dogs.

"So they got him," said the man bitterly. "I told him not to register."

He extricated himself out of the fur blankets and jumped down from the sleigh. He covered his horse and hung a feed bag over his head.

"I am Bogdan Kowalski. My wife, Sonia."

Vita introduced herself. Then Kowalski and his wife followed Vita into the house. She began telling them about George and his family, about her desperate situation, the fears that were gnawing at her, and the overwhelming anxiety she lived with not knowing what do to next. She went on and on, spewing all her frustrations on two complete strangers who were obviously both fascinated and horrified by her story.

"I am sorry," she finally checked herself. "I haven't seen a human being for so long...."

"Oh, please don't apologize," said the woman. "We understand. Look, maybe there is something we can do to help."

Sipping hot coffee, which Vita hastily prepared, they sat there thinking the situation over.

"What is happening with the war?" Vita asked.

"Oh, for us Poles it's all over."

The man then brought Vita up to date, at least all he knew, about the war, now raging on all fronts. The British and French were in it; it was going to be a long time before things got back to normal.

"And you heard about Warsaw, didn't you?" he asked.

"Yes, the last we heard they were still holding on."

"Well, it's all over now. Starzynski gave up the city September 27th, and just as well. It was in ruins and the casualties were unbelievable. The Government had gone to Rumania with all the gold they could haul, and we are at the mercy of the Communists! I don't know what to tell you, my dear lady, only that we live not too far from here, and we will certainly keep in touch from now on. The snow hasn't been too heavy this winter; the roads are passable — you could even walk the distance between our houses on a nice day like today. We just have to sit tight, keep a low profile, try to get through the winter, and, most of all, hope the Russians won't find us," he said.

"Why are they taking people out of their homes and where are they shipping them?" Vita wanted to know.

"Well, there are different opinions. Some people think the Russians are reclaiming this land which once belonged to them. We only had this eastern portion of Byelorussia for the last twenty years. They will most certainly resettle it with their own people, so when a general plebiscite is held, it will be voted into the USSR 'fair and square.'"

"But don't you think the League of Nations has something to say about it?" Vita asked.

"Oh, you know how that works — they don't mind carving up a small country, just to appease the big ones," he said dejectedly.

Vita turned the conversation to a more pressing subject — food. She told the man that the supplies of staples were getting quite low. George took a large portion when he left and, most of all, she was worried about feeding the chickens, the dogs, the pig and the horse. There was plenty of hay, but the grain was down to almost nothing, and there was not much other food left.

"Mrs. Nadvorny had a cellar full of preserves, canned fruit, vegetables and pickles, but try and feed that to a pack of hungry dogs," she said. "I have been cooking a large pot of kasza and potatoes every day, and we have been getting by, but we have no meat of any kind. There is still some lard and bacon left, but it won't last very long."

Bogdan Kowalski talked the situation over with his wife and finally declared, "We have plenty of supplies, so don't worry about you and your daughter going hungry, and as far as the animals are concerned, we can take the horse, and the dogs with us — we have a couple of those ourselves. The pig, however, will be a problem. There isn't any way I can transport him. He must weight at least 200 pounds, and besides he should be butchered."

"Oh, please don't let Ellie hear that," whispered Vita. "She would just as soon starve than eat him!"

"Just give me a couple of days to figure something out. In the meantime, I will replenish your staples and get some fresh meat for you. Are these chickens you have there laying eggs?"

"Not now," said Vita. "We had some eggs last fall. Ellie is taking care of them. I really don't know what one does to make them produce eggs!"

"Well, we will fix that," he said. "So let's get going; there is much to be done."

Ellie wasn't happy about giving up the animals, but Bogdan Kowalski promised she could see them anytime she wanted to and they would be well taken care of. The three dachshunds jumped happily into the back of the sleigh, and Mrs. Kowalski took the long lead rope and tied the old chestnut to the back of the sleigh.

"Well, goodbye for now. We will be back tomorrow. And, Ellie, you can come with us tomorrow, if you like."

They waved their goodbyes and moved down the road at a slow pace. You could hear the sleigh bells for a long while.

"I am going there tomorrow," Ellie announced. "I want to see for myself. These are strangers, Mother. You don't know anything about them. How do you know they will take care of the dogs and the horse?"

"Ellie, be reasonable. They are friends of the Nadvornys, and besides they did us a big favor. You know how little food there is left to feed us all."

Ellie turned on her heel and went in, closing the den door behind her.

****

The next day Bogdan came back with a large supply of staples and a hare ready to be roasted. He reported to Ellie that the old horse was quite at home in his new barn and very happy to have a companion. The dogs were fine too.

"You are welcome to come and visit them anytime you want to," he told her.

After the man left, Vita hastily got the hare into the oven. Ellie was carrying wood into the house for the three stoves.

"What are you cooking, Mother?"

"Oh, it's a very large hen Mr. Kowalski brought us, sweetheart. We are going to have a good dinner! Go in and read for a while. I will call you when it's ready."

She knew she would have to carve up the meat in such a way that it would not resemble a bunny in the least. Ellie would not touch it if she knew what it was, but eat she must, thought Vita. She had lost enough weight already.

****

February, 1940. The Kowalskis became frequent visitors. Ellie learned how to drive the one-horse sleigh, maneuvering it well down the narrow path through the woods. Life again settled into a routine, as the days grew longer with very little additional snow and slightly warmer temperatures. Nights, however, were still very cold, the skies were clear, bright with stars and the stillness was almost eerie. Smoke from the chimneys on the little cottage rose straight up into the sky like a ribbon. Smoke! The smoke! Vita stopped admiring the night. The realization of what these thin ribbons in the sky meant came crashing down on her with such force she could hear her heart pound. How foolish she had been thinking that nobody would ever know this cottage was being lived in! But then what alternative did she have?

From that time on, she somehow knew that their days were numbered. It was just a matter of time. She even considered approaching the new Russian authority, whoever they were, explaining her situation to them and asking for help. After all, she was a Swiss citizen, not a local resident. But Bogdan Kowalski strongly urged her against it.

"Mrs. Kew," he said, "you don't know the Communists and the way they operate. They don't care who you are. They have their orders and they will follow them no matter what. Human lives mean nothing to them. Stalin is another beast, like Hitler, and he rules with an iron fist. He wants this land and he is going to annex it to the USSR by hook or by crook."

"Well, let him have it!" Vita was now openly crying. "I really don't care. All I want is to go home!"

Kowalski didn't know how to console her. He understood her plight, but there was nothing he could do to help her or, for that matter, himself. It was just a "wait and see" situation.

****

12

A TRIP TO HELL

*"On the night of February 10th, 1940,
during one night 200,000 people were taken by
force out of their homes and shipped into
Northern and Eastern Soviet Union, 760,000 others to follow.
For many this was a sentence of death."*

Translated from:
WE THE DEPORTED
by Bogdan Klukowski

February 10, 1940. She thought she had mentally prepared herself for the time when they would come to get her, but when the night finally came and loud blows on the door brought her and Ellie to their feet, she was numb with fear.

"Open up! Don't be afraid. We are here to help, not to harm you!" a man's voice yelled.

Vita opened the door and three armed Russian soldiers entered. The officer spoke some Polish.

"We are with the repatriation unit of the Soviet Army. Get ready. We have very little time."

As he was trying to communicate with Vita, two armed soldiers went through the house, searching.

"There is no one else here," came the report from one of them.

The officer then ordered them out of the house.

"Put some tea on the stove," he said to Vita. "It is beastly cold out there."

She obeyed his order. She was almost paralyzed with fear.

She gathered up enough courage and asked, "When are we supposed to move?"

He looked at her incredulously. "Right now! There are trucks waiting outside, so get dressed, pack your things and after I have had my tea we shall go!"

"What do you mean, now?" Vita was beside herself. "It's the middle of the night! You frightened us to death. My child is ill! I can't take her out into the cold. There must be some mistake."

"There is no mistake. Everybody must go!"

He was getting angry. "So get busy!"

She poured a large cup of tea for him, and he stirred three heaping spoons of sugar into it and slurped it loudly. Convinced that there was no other way, Vita started to get ready. She bundled up as much warm clothing as she could carry, found her own suitcase and glanced at it thoughtfully. Across the lid there was a succession of rips where machine gun bullets had crazed the leather.

"Ellie, please get yourself dressed as warmly as possible. Put on your boots and breeches and that sheepskin jacket and hat."

Ellie scurried around, got dressed, put on two sweaters, mittens and a muffler.

"Mother, let's roll up this crib mattress. It might be nice to sit on."

"Remember," said the officer, "take only what you can carry." He spoke very deliberately using as many Polish words as he knew to make himself understood.

Thank God, Mother knows enough of both these languages, thought Ellie, because most of it is Greek to me.

"I'll have your papers now," said the officer.

Vita got them out of her handbag and handed them to him. He opened the passports and a look of shocked surprise and suspicion came over his face. "Swiss? What is this? Where did you get these? Who are you?"

All of a sudden his mild manner was gone. He snatched Vita's handbag from her hands and spilled the contents onto the table going through them one by one.

"Yuri, come in here!" he yelled. The door opened, and a soldier carrying a rifle entered. "Get two of your men in here and search this house again!"

It all happened so fast, Vita was speechless. Her eyes darted to the handbag. "Lieutenant, I don't understand. What's wrong? And please may I have my bag back?"

She desperately tried to stay calm. Inside the handbag, under the lining, neatly sewn back together, was a small fortune in jewelry and money. I can't have anything happen to it, she thought, we will need every penny once we get back. Dear God, let me be calm.

"Lieutenant, may I explain," said Vita in a level voice, gathering the things slowly and putting them back. "You see, my daughter and I came to Poland in August, last year, from Switzerland, just for a vacation. My husband's family lives near Torun, and we were visiting them when the war broke out."

The lieutenant looked up sharply. "Where is your husband now? Is he here?"

"Oh, no. He is in Switzerland. It's just the two of us."

She struggled with the language; he strained to comprehend what she was trying to tell him. The handbag, now neatly repacked, sat on the table under her watchful eye.

"Well, never mind. This does not change your status." The officer waved his men off and turned to leave. "Come along, we have lost a lot of time."

Vita gathered her bag, suitcase, all the available food in a net-like sack, a thermos with water, put on the warmest coat she had, tied a wool scarf around her head and, leaving the room, glanced back. She thought sadly of the Nadvornys. She felt grateful to them for everything they had done for her. She did not know what had happened to them, but their home had given her and Ellie shelter and warmth for a short while.

There were two military lorries parked outside. One was almost filled with shadowy figures wrapped in blankets, huddled together.

"Make room," a soldier yelled, "two more people coming in. You there," he nudged one form with his boot, "move over!"

Vita got into the dark lorry and found a seat. Ellie passed up some of the belongings and the food, then hopped on, squeezing next to her mother. Somebody was talking to Vita in Yiddish, touching her arm. She moved away and said she did not understand. Then the man spoke in Polish. He wanted to know who she was and where they were going. He was an old man with long frizzy hair and a beard, his bony fingers still grabbing Vita's arm.

"Please," Vita said, "I don't know anymore than you do, and I am very tired."

She moved as far away from him as she could, squeezing Ellie into the corner. Somebody across from her was smoking a cigarette. In the glow she could see another bearded face, and further away a few women, covered up with blankets. Who were they? she wondered. They looked like Orthodox Jews. The lorry was now moving. Two armed guards stood on the running board, at the very back.

"Mother, where are they taking us?" whispered Ellie.

"I don't know. Here, cover up."

She put her arm around her daughter and brought her as close as she could, shielding her from the cold air whipping through the open back.

It took over an hour to reach their destination, the railroad station in Pinsk. They were unloaded onto the platform, joining hordes of other people, all lined up in front of a long freight train. The front cars were already being loaded. Guards shoved people, threw their bundles up to them and shouted, "Forty to a car!"

Then a loud clang on the large sliding door signaled each filled car. Their turn finally came. Two guards helped them up.

"Pick a place on either shelf, up or down," they shouted.

The scrambling crowd rushed in claiming a small section, just large enough for a body to lie down on the straw-lined surface. Vita pushed Ellie ahead of her to a corner spot, on the lower shelf and stacked their belongings there. She sat down close to the girl and took a horrified look around her. She had never seen anything like it. The freight train, she assumed to be a cattle train, was nothing like that at all. These freight cars were built to transport prisoners! But why? Were there so many criminals in Russia? She had known all along about the forced labor camps in Siberia, Uzbekistan and Kazahkstan, but never realized what it meant.

By the dim light of a hanging lantern, she could see most of her new "accommodations." Across the end of each freight car there were two shelves, one about five feet high, the other two and a half feet, both filled with straw. The lower shelf projected further out from the end so that one could climb up to the top shelf or use it to sit on. Ten people were expected to sleep on these shelves, side by side. At either end of the top shelf was a long, narrow window which slid open to allow fresh air, but was not large enough for a person to squeeze through. At the center of the car, on one side only, there was a large sliding door for loading and unloading people. The small open center area accommodated two benches, a pile of wood, a barrel of water and a cast iron stove with a flat top on which sat a large tea kettle. Behind the woodpile was a small partition which screened a hole in the floor which, when the train was moving, was used as a toilet. Vita had no idea how one managed to use it. Next to the hole stood a container with foul smelling white powder, a disinfectant, to be sprinkled around the hole and washed down with water stored there in a drum-like container. It was degrading and disgusting! I hope to God, the trip doesn't last very long, she thought, smoothing down the straw and covering it with a blanket.

Ellie's cold seemed to be in full bloom now. Her cough was dry, cheeks flushed, and all she wanted was some tea or water.

"Why don't you lie down for a while. It's only four in the morning," suggested Vita, folding a coat and a blanket to serve as a pillow.

Theirs were the last two spaces on the lower shelf. Ellie crawled up and lay down, pushing her back as close to the car's wall as she could. Somebody had started a fire in the stove and pungent smoke filled the car. A man on an upper shelf slid one of the windows open to air it out. Vita got up from her bunk and rinsed out the tea kettle, filling it with water and putting it on the stove. She had brought with her some tea, coffee, sugar and a jar of honey.

"Here is some hot tea, sweetheart." She handed Ellie a large cup, stirring in some honey.

Their car, now loaded to capacity, was being checked by a guard who counted the bodies.

"Okay here," he yelled to someone on the platform. The door was then slammed shut, sending shivers through Vita. There was such finality in the loud clang, not unlike a jail gate closing behind criminals. Vita spent the rest of the early morning hours wide awake. Huddled next to Ellie, she tried desperately to make some sense out of all this. What next? How does one survive this? Where were they going? And the conditions! She looked around at the rows of bodies, squeezed like sardines, one stranger next to another, sleeping on lumpy straw, like animals. How degrading and inhumane. She rebelled inwardly at the entire process of treatment. The arrests — always in the middle of the night, when people were the most vulnerable, unprepared, half-asleep. A beastly method of imposing power over innocent people. Oh, she had a story to tell the world when.... Yes, when? She despaired. She did not know then that 220,000 people were sharing her fate that same night!

Finally she could hear the huffs and puffs of a locomotive which, after a few jolts, hooked up to the train. It rammed the cars so hard that one had to hold on to something, not to fall. The train was moving slowly, pulling the long line of cars, changing rails back and forth and finally stopping again. Vita had forgotten to wind her watch, so she had no idea what time it was, but through the narrow cracks of the car's walls, she could see daylight.

The big sliding train door opened with a bang and two armed soldiers appeared in the sunlit, wide gap. An infant cried somewhere on the other side of the car, and its mother could be heard trying to shush it, unsuccessfully.

"Everybody out!" yelled a guard. Several bodies started to move from the straw-filled shelves, fully clothed, bundled up against the cold, pushing toward the opening.

"Ellie, we'd better go outside now; do you have to go to the bathroom?"

"Yes. Do you know where we are?"

"We are still in Pinsk. Haven't moved much during the night...." Vita jumped off the train car, hanging onto Ellie's hand. They walked to an area designated by the armed guard, where already dozens of squatting figures could be seen, defecating on the white, glistening snow — a ridiculous and disgusting sight. She felt nauseous.

"Ellie, let's scoot under this car to the other side — it's more private there."

The guard yelled at them not to wander off too far. So, this was to be their bathroom facility when the train was not moving, she wondered.

When they got back, an army field kitchen was distributing "breakfast" — one slice of heavy, black bread, per person, and hot water. The guards assigned two men to the task and the meager rations were distributed in no time.

****

They were now traveling a few hours at a time, stopping for meals or waiting on sidetracks to let other trains pass through. Vita's tiny glimmer of hope, that maybe they were, in fact, being taken back beyond the Curzon Line, died when the train pulled into a railroad station and the sign on one of the buildings read MINSK. Her head reeled. She suppressed a sick feeling in the pit of her stomach. Her hands felt clammy. They are taking us to RUSSIA! There was no doubt about that anymore. But why? What have we done? Was it punishment? If so, what for?

She could not comprehend any of this. Here she was, a woman alone with a 14-year-old girl, on this hideous train carrying thousands of wretched people, God knows where and why! What was she to do? Could she grab Ellie and run into the city and beg for help? Surely Minsk had a Swiss consulate. Maybe somebody would be able to help them.

"Hey, you," the guard was yelling. "Time's up, back on the train, come on, come on, hurry!"

Ellie joined her promptly, and arm in arm they walked toward their car.

"We are going to Siberia, aren't we?" Ellie asked.

"I really don't know," replied Vita. "We are certainly headed northeast, but where we end up, God only knows."

Their attention was drawn to a small group of people arguing excitedly. A couple of women were crying loudly, grabbing on to a young man who tried to fight them off.

"No, Mark, no, please!" a woman screamed.

The young man broke loose, scampered up an embankment, slipping on the snow and ice.

Then the guard yelled, "Halt, you there, come back."

The boy kept running. Two shots rang out in rapid succession, followed by a few seconds of complete silence and then a wild scream. Yells and curses broke out all over. Several women and a couple of old men reached the boy, crying and lamenting in Yiddish. They were oblivious to the orders of the guards, who were now six or seven in number. One of the women sat down on the snow, picked the boy's head up and laid it in her lap. The guards were frantically herding the rest of the crowd toward the train.

"You filthy murderers," hissed Vita through clenched teeth. "You...."

There were no words she could think of that would express her anger, frustration and a desperate feeling of complete helplessness. Ellie was crying quietly. As they reached their freight car, they noticed that the familiar queue was forming from a water pump on one side and a woodpile on the other. Wood and water were being passed from hand to hand onto the train. Ellie wiped off her tears and took a place in the wood line. She must be frightened half to death, poor thing, thought Vita. The attention of the workers was not on their immediate task. They were all stealing glances toward the activity where the shooting had taken place. Some local authority, in uniform other than the guards, was now on the scene, but the prisoners couldn't make out what was going on. Was the boy dead? What were they going to do with him? What about his family? Were they going to leave him behind?

A nice-looking, tall blond man came over and stood next to Vita.

"I am Jan Wozniak," he whispered. "Don't concern yourself with this incident too much. Remember, our main goal is our own survival. As you know, we are being taken into Russia, probably to a detention or labor camp. Is it just you and your daughter?"

Vita nodded.

"I have a wife and two little girls in the next car. I am trying to get permission from the officer in charge of this train to get us regrouped a little. I am sure you noticed that almost all of the prisoners here are Orthodox Jews from Galicia who speak only Yiddish.

There are maybe twenty or so Christian families on this entire train. We were the first to arrive at the station, so I had plenty of opportunity to observe all the others. They are mostly Jewish merchants, shop keepers, rabbis, etc. I will do my best to get us moved together; and if there is anything I can do to help, I hope you will let me know. It's in our best interest to stick together and help each other. My younger daughter is only three years old and my heart breaks when I think of what's in store for her."

How nice he was. Vita found out later he was a faculty member from the University of Warsaw and, like everybody else, fled the city after it was almost leveled by German bombers and fire. He had found himself in the eastern zone and was "rescued" by the Russians and now was traveling east, just like she was, toward an unknown fate!

The wood loaded up and the water barrels filled, the guards urged everybody to get back to their places because breakfast was being brought to the train. A huge army truck made its way along the platform, stopping at each car and two steaming cauldrons were passed up. This morning, in addition to the soggy black bread, there was porridge. It was quickly distributed to the passengers who ate their breakfast in silence.

Vita went to the stove and brought back two cups of scalding water to which she added a pinch of tea and a tiny bit of sugar from her suitcase of supplies. She was indeed lucky to have taken some of the dry goods along. As she looked around, she noticed that almost every family had a bundle containing similar goods — tea, sugar, biscuits, tins of cocoa, some conserves. Ellie wasn't hungry; she just drank her tea.

"You have got to eat this porridge whether you like it or not," Vita admonished. "If we are to somehow survive this, we have got to have strength — both of us! I will need you to help me carry our things when we get off this train. You can't expect me to do it all!"

"All right. All right." Ellie was almost gagging with each swallow.

"Wait a minute." Vita reached into the sack again and brought out a jar of honey and dabbed the porridge with it. It went down much easier, and Ellie managed a small smile and a thank you. She then wrapped the two slices of bread in a linen towel and put them away with the rest of her provisions. Food was distributed to the train cars only twice a day. The bread would have to be eaten at "lunch" time with another cup of tea. The best way to consume the heavy, soggy bread was to place it on the stove's flat surface and toast it. It became quite good, particularly when you sprinkled it with sugar or dabbed it with honey.

Vita was up again, washing out their wooden bowls and spoons, dumping the water into the hole, behind the partition. The train was still standing, but the whistles and puffs of locomotives could be heard close by. One of them would soon hook up to the train and they would be on their way. It was still quite early in the morning. Judging by the previous days, they would probably travel five or six hours and then stop again for their evening meal and outing.

The heavy sliding door was being rolled shut, and the guard latched it noisily. The narrow, high windows provided enough light on a bright day to read by, particularly on the higher shelf, positioned directly under it. Ellie sat cross-legged in the middle of her space, braiding her long hair. The light reflected from her coppery head, and Vita's heart ached when she looked at the thin, pale face with dark circles under the eyes. If she were only healthy, she thought, and that hair! It will have to be cut off if this journey is to last any length of time. It can't be kept clean in these conditions, particularly in the winter.

****

The old rabbi started his prayers. His book lay open on his knees, but he didn't read from it. His eyes were closed, and he kept moving his body back and forth in a steady motion. Once in a while he would give the ceiling an agonizing look and a sort of chant emanated from his lips. Then he would go back to the same motion. Presently several men and women joined him and soon there was moaning all over, and everybody was bobbing back and forth. A sudden noisy jerk of the car sent the whole group sprawling to the floor, a grotesque sight. Brace yourself, thought Vita, here comes another. It took the train and the locomotive several tries to hook up and finally it started moving, slowly, laboriously, onto the next leg of its journey.

From the day of the shooting incident, the cars were aired one at a time. This permitted a heavier concentration of guards and better supervision, but cut the outing time considerably. Vita did not get another opportunity to see the nice man from the next car although she looked for him every time they were permitted to go outside. Ellie's cold was almost gone, thank God, and the two of them looked forward to the walk and the fresh air, twice a day.

The morale in their car deteriorated with each day. The moaning prayers became more frequent and the air more stale and putrid with the diminishing effort at cleanliness and order. The days fell into a routine with just one variant — the evening meal. It was soup, sometimes potato, red beet, cabbage or fish, in no particular order. Ellie dreaded the fish nights the most. It took almost all of Vita's strength and patience to get some of the soup down her throat. She would gag and cry, "Just look at this! There are heads, bones and even eyes swimming in there."

Finally she absolutely refused to eat it. There was nothing Vita could do. She would rather go hungry; she would rather die, she said, than swallow another ounce of the filthy stuff. And that was that! There was no use fighting her.

****

The mark on Vita's calendar indicated that they had now spent sixteen days on the road and February was almost over. The constant nagging question kept cropping up. How much longer? Vita eyed her remaining provisions with alarm. There was not much more left of the sugar, tea and other delicacies totally absent from the train's menu. If this trip lasts much longer, she thought, my supplies will be gone. She dreaded the thought of drinking hot water instead of tea, eating dry bread.

The days were not as bad as the nights. During the light hours, Vita always found something to keep herself busy. There were things to wash and dry and she could knit.

"What's it going to be today?" Ellie would laugh. "Part of a mitten or hat?"

The "thing" would really never be anything because there was only one large ball of yarn and two needles which Vita threw into her bag when packing; so after knitting furiously for hours, she would run out of yarn, rip it all out and start over again. The yarn was becoming a little frayed, but that did not discourage her. Vita Kew was a doer, and to keep her sanity she had to work at something. Ellie couldn't count the times her mother repacked their belongings, arranging them one way or another.

Early one morning, after one of those sleepless nights, a terrible scream made them jump right up.

"My baby! Oh, my God, my baby is dead! She is dead!"

It was the young girl, Elsa. Vita didn't know her last name. Poor thing! She did her best caring for the month-old infant. Vita remembered her constant requests for milk, but the guards did not have any, and the army field kitchen had no food suitable for small babies, so all they could tell her was, "It won't be long anymore, and where you are going, there will be plenty of milk."

So she waited and waited trying in vain to nurse the baby at her dry breast. Vita felt pangs of pity and sorrow for the poor, young mother. This was murder! Somebody should be accountable for it, she thought bitterly, watching the girl's agony. The women close to her tried to take the infant from her but she held on, begging them not to take it.

The train finally came to a stop — regular morning routine, doors opened wide, armed guards on duty. Elsa, clutching her dead baby, rushed forward toward the open door. She brought the bundle up to the guard's face and screamed, "Here, look at her, look at my dead baby!"

She was out of her head, her face contorted into a wild expression.

"No milk, no food — look what you have done! I hope all your own babies die."

She was grabbed by two soldiers as she almost leaped out of the car. They felt sorry for her and tried to calm her down. One of the guards tried to take the baby away from her, but she recoiled and spat in his face.

"Don't you touch her!" she screamed.

They led her away from the train toward the tiny railroad station, a pathetic figure, yet unafraid. What else could happen to her that would be worse than this? She didn't care any longer.

Gloom had settled on the passengers. Shaken by the scene, they went about their business in silence and dejection. Vita and Ellie went outside for their walk and fresh air, but their hearts were not in it. As they stood to the side of the entrance, a guard approached them and in a low voice said to Vita, "Get your things ready. During the evening stop you will be transferred to the next car. Your relatives are there, and you will be better off with them."

Jan Wozniak had kept his word! Vita was elated.

"Ellie, did you hear that? We will join that nice family in the next car."

She could hardly wait to get back into the train to start gathering their belongings.

"Ellie, hurry up, don't just stand there! We have a lot to do."

Ellie looked at her mother in wonderment. A little baby was dead, everyone was surely doomed. There was no way to survive this. They would all perish sooner or later, but her mother was only concerned with the immediate task of getting out of one car, moving into another, and being with some other strangers who, to her, were no better or worse than the ones she was surrounded by now. Sure, they were all Jewish, most of them spoke only Yiddish and looked funny in their black Orthodox garb, but what difference did it make?

She was almost shoved into the train by her mother's eager hands and given a battery of orders: "Please, don't daydream; don't you understand this is a break for us. We will be with people who are like us."

"Oh, Mother, what difference does it make? Besides, how do you know what kind of people the others are. You don't know them; they may be worse."

Vita's large gray eyes had a strange glint in them. There was such determination in her clenched jaws, giving that beautiful face of hers an expression Ellie hadn't seen before. It frightened her.

"All right, Mother, what do you want me to do?"

The time passed very slowly. After breakfast they started putting their belongings together in bundles, bags and the suitcase which now served as a pantry. All the remaining goodies were carefully packed and the suitcase was tied with a length of twine for extra safety. The people around them did not pay any attention to the activity. Vita was always rearranging her things; they were used to her packing and unpacking. When she was finally satisfied that everything was ready, she settled down with her knitting, going at it with a vengeance.

Time dragged on. At noon they roasted their bread, had a cup of tea and waited. The train seemed to be traveling at a good clip, and Ellie wondered where they were. Minsk was far behind them. That was the last large city they passed that she could recognize. She remembered her geography. Moscow was the capital and was located somewhat in the western part of the vast country. They were moving east; the sun was setting almost directly behind the train. She must look at her mother's calendar to see how many days they had been traveling. Maybe somebody could ask that nice guard; he should know.

The train finally came to a stop. Slowly, with much whistling and puffing, it moved onto a side track. The locomotive unhooked itself and puffed away. That usually meant they would spend the night. The doors opened and Vita eagerly looked for the guard who spoke to her that morning. He was there! After most of the people got off, he waved to Vita. He even gave them a hand with their bundles as they walked toward the next car. The occupants were all outside. Jan Wozniak came right over and helped them up into his car. Vita immediately noticed that there were not as many people in there.

Jan pointed to a spacious place in the corner, on the upper shelf and said, "You can put your things over there. My wife and I and our two girls are right next to you. This whole half of the car is ours. The Jews are on the other side. There are only fifteen of them and they keep pretty much to themselves. One of them is a doctor from Warsaw and he is very competent and levelheaded. When everybody is back from the outing, you will meet them all. There are five Catholic families here and, as far as I could see, maybe twenty or thirty more on the entire train."

One by one, the remaining passengers came in and Jan introduced them to Vita and Ellie. There were two young girls among them. One probably a couple of years older than Ellie and another, a couple of years younger. Vita was elated.

Ellie would have company; the girls could do things together; what a stroke of luck.

The introductions went on. "This is Stan Kucharski and his wife, Marta, and their son, Marian."

Stan was a rough looking man, in his middle forties, very strong and muscular, with a bowlegged stance and a no-nonsense attitude. He was apparently blind in one eye. A milky substance covered the cornea, giving him a somewhat sinister appearance. But as soon as he grabbed their hands, shook them vigorously and said, "Welcome, welcome," all their apprehensions disappeared. He was a friendly, simple man with a broad, engaging smile and warm personality. His wife, Marta, was a typical housewife, on the plumpish side, rather shy and not too attractive. Their son, Marian, sixteen or seventeen years old, didn't resemble either parent. He was very tall, lanky and self-assured. He had blond, curly hair and large brown eyes, and next to his burly father he appeared rather slight and effeminate.

"Our oldest boy died in the war," said Marta. "He was nineteen! We also have a married daughter, somewhere in Poland. I see there are just the two of you. Oh, dear God, what is happening to us all?"

"Now, now, let's not start this again." Stan wrapped his arm around her and patted her reassuringly.

He winked at the others with his good eye and said, "It's been a terrible ordeal for her. The children have always been her whole world."

He led her toward the bench near the stove where Marian was making a cup of tea for his mother. Jan handed the bedding and other bundles up to Vita who arranged them the best she could. There being more room in the car, the upper shelves were used as sleeping quarters and the lower as a sitting facility. This was a much more comfortable arrangement. Vita also noticed that their half was very neatly swept, things put away, the water barrel had a cover on it and no foul odor emanated from the hole.

Evidently the families who had men along were able to take more things with them because their possessions, by comparison with Vita's, were much greater. For example, there was some linen on the pillows, feather beds, towels and even a small kerosene lamp. There were also two lines stretched between the bunks in one corner; evidently things got washed and dried there. The stove was flanked by two benches where one could sit and warm oneself, or maybe one ate there. Vita liked what she saw.

Ellie was already talking with one of the young girls, Anya Karowska, and found out that Anya spoke French. She and her mother, Greta, were also alone; their father, a Colonel in the Polish Army, was somewhere, they knew not where, lost or perhaps dead. Anya, like Ellie, was an only child and glad of it.

"At least there is nobody else to worry about," she would say.

The girls were engrossed in conversation, seemingly oblivious to everything around them. Anya was blond and very pretty. Her hair was cut short but not very well. Vita wondered about it, looking around. All the women and children had very short hair, clean and well combed.

"It's all been cut on the train," she decided.

Presently three young children entered the car. There was such a resemblance among them, it was obvious they were a family — a boy sixteen, and two girls, twelve and eight. They were alone. Their parents and their youngest brother were all killed by a bomb in their own home in Warsaw. The three children, who were with their grand-parents in a suburb at that time, were orphaned on the first day of the war, during one of the first raids on that city. They were then forcibly evacuated by the government from the embattled area and sent east to escape the bombs. What followed was more or less the same as all the other stories. They were now alone.

Jerzy, the oldest, assumed responsibility for his two younger sisters, Nella and Dorotka. Their sleeping space was in the other corner. You could see that the children had very little with them, probably just the clothes they wore, a couple of blankets and an old raggedy doll that Dorotka wouldn't let go of, night or day. Marta Kucharska evidently had been given the task of supervising these children because, as soon as they came back from their outing, she busied herself over the stove. She poured hot cocoa into three cups and handed it to them.

"It's much colder out there today," said Jerzy. "I tried to run in place like Mr. Wozniak told me, but my hands and face got very cold."

Vita noticed that he did not have any gloves or a hat. Poor thing, she thought, he must freeze out there. All of a sudden she knew what she would knit next out of the ball of blue yarn. A cap for Jerzy! She had no time to start on her new project because the field kitchen came to a screeching stop outside the car and soup was announced by the guard.

Jan Wozniak leaned out and shouted to two other people who were slowly walking back from their outing. They were elderly and one of them moved with great difficulty, supporting himself on a cane and hanging onto the arm of the other. They were Mr. and Mrs. Kos. Theirs was a similar story. They owned a small grocery store in a town near Warsaw; and when the bombs came, they fled with as many belongings as they could carry and finally were picked up by the Russians with the identical promise as all the others, that they would be shipped back home. Mr. Kos, a feisty little man, angered a Russian soldier with a few swear words and was badly beaten up. Nobody knew the extent of his injuries until they were assigned to the train where the doctor looked him over and patched some of the wounds the best he could. He was still very weak, but was determined to navigate on his own. So, twice a day, with the help of the men and his wife, he bundled up and went outside for a walk to breathe some good air, as he put it. When everybody was gathered around the stove, the cauldron with soup was passed up and Marta Kucharska filled the bowls. Soup du jour was potato.

"Oh, thank God, it isn't fish!" exclaimed Ellie with delight.

Everybody laughed at her obvious relief. Vita looked around the circle of her new friends and companions and she liked what she saw. She was particularly happy with the young group. There were four of the older children sitting on one bench, eating their meal and talking animatedly. Three of the little ones were sitting next to Maria Wozniak, who made sure that all food was eaten up, none wasted.

She is awfully thin and looks so unhealthy, thought Vita, examining the wife of her "benefactor." She was very short, with mousy sparse blond hair that framed her sallow-complexioned face with thin wavy strands. The dour expression on her face didn't help her appearance any. "I wonder if she ever smiles?"

Her glance now shifted to Maria's husband, Jan. Tall, blond and handsome. He grew a beard that was trimmed very carefully, quite close to his face, giving the long face a better dimension. Vita wondered if this was intentional. He had an air about him that signaled self-assurance and a hint of vanity. How did those two ever pair up, she wondered. They had two little daughters. The older, a tomboy of eight, constantly on the move, hyperactive, a nuisance. She was into everything at once and all the nagging of her mother and admonitions of her father didn't faze her a bit. Krista was a brat. Her younger sister, Elzunia, on the other hand, was the loveliest little creature Vita had ever seen. She was blond like her father with an angelic little face and large blue eyes. She was quiet, obedient and obviously adored by both parents.

The soup all eaten, Maria was now washing the little girls' hands and wiping their faces. Mrs. Kos walked over from her seat and, reaching into a sack, brought out a few colorfully wrapped hard candies which she distributed, one to each child. A loud chorus of thank-you followed. Ellie jumped up from her seat and came over to her mother.

"Here, you have half. It will make your tea taste much better," she said.

"Oh, thank you, dear, but I really don't want it. You have it."

"You sure?"

"Yes, I am positive!"

"Okay," said Ellie and popped the candy into her mouth. She crossed her eyes and grinned from ear to ear. It brought laughs around the group. What a clown, thought Vita.

After clearing away the supper things, the group gathered around Jan who spread a crude, makeshift map on the bench. He had drawn the map at the beginning of the journey and each day marked the date on the margin and drew a line showing the train's progress. It was quite impossible to guess the distance their train covered each day. Unless they passed a known town, they really had no idea where they were. He had gotten some information from the guard whom he had bribed some time ago. Vita found out that he had given him his watch with a gold bracelet and that the guard was bowled over by such a generous gift. Neither he, nor anybody he knew, had ever owned such a handsome watch, and it ran and kept good time, and it was real gold! He had done many favors already for this wonderful gift and felt that he was still indebted to Wozniak. He promised he would do anything he could to help him and his "family."

"Let's see, this is March 1st," said Wozniak, "and we have been moving northeast from Minsk now for approximately eighteen days. We haven't passed any large towns or places I can orient myself by, but I think we must be approaching Moscow. True, we were traveling just a few miles on some days and most of the nights were spent sitting on side tracks, but still, we have been underway for almost three weeks. We have got to be close to Moscow."

MOSCOW! A feeling of wonderment came over the group. That's quite a distance from the Polish border. Where do you think we will end up, they asked one another. Jan folded the map carefully.

"I will have a talk with that friendly guard tomorrow," he said. "He may be able to find out for us where this train is headed. How about some bridge now? Mrs. Kew, you play, don't you?"

"Yes," said Vita, amazed at the lighthearted way Jan disposed of a very grave matter. "Yes, I would like to...."

"All right then. Children, you can kibitz if you want to. Every civilized young lady ought to know how to play bridge. Here is a good opportunity to learn."

He moved one of the benches to face the other and placed an empty suitcase on the players' knees. The little oil lamp was lit and soon the group was engrossed in the game. Vita drew Mrs. Karowska for her partner. She had just barely met her. The woman was tall, gaunt and used her long bony fingers with great dexterity when she shuffled the cards. She was very sure of herself and every time she spoke to Vita, she spoke in French which annoyed Maria Wozniak, who did not know the language. She had a long, aristocratic nose and shrewd eyes set rather close together. Her lips were thin and pale and she had a habit of talking out of the corner of her mouth. I wouldn't like to cross her, thought Vita.

The children were all stretched out on the upper bunk on their stomachs, some of them looking at the cards from their high perch. Ellie did not like card games of any kind, so she and Anya were telling each other stories about their schools, home towns, fathers, families, anything. There was so much to tell. They prattled on into the evening.

That night, after settling down to sleep, Vita experienced a peculiar sensation of wanting to thank somebody for the way things, bad as they were, had turned out. She had profusely thanked Jan and Maria and offered to contribute a watch, ring or money to further bribe the guard, but that, somehow, wasn't enough. She thought of God. Her relationship with the Almighty was never a very close one. She knew He was there, somewhere. She knew also that certain things were directly attributable to Him, but she could never accept the total submission that her religion demanded of her. Good or bad, you took it and accepted it because the Lord knew what He was doing. That's a lot of rot! she thought. You mean to tell me that this good and kind divine creature sits up there and dishes out lots to His people? Here take this! You will lose one of your legs tomorrow, but you will pray to me and you will be grateful that you haven't lost both! Oh, and you...your house will fall on you when the bombs fly, and you and your little children will all die agonizing deaths trying to claw their way out of the rubble.

She was now half asleep.

"Help! Oh, dear God, help me!" The words were ringing in her ears. A bloody hand and arm sticking out of the stones and bricks and the voice from under there....

"Ellie, for God's sake, leave him. You can't do anything for him." She was grabbing the girl's arm and pulling her away from the mound with the voice in it. She struggled with her, dragging her into the orchard that bordered the small hotel, now burning and partially crumbled under the hit. They ran as fast as they could manage and finally fell, head first into a drainage ditch, when again they heard the ominous scream of the bombs that exploded with ear shattering....

"Mother, Mother, wake up, you are having the nightmare again!"

Ellie was shaking her arm.

"Oh, all right, I am fine, I am awake." She sat up in her bunk drenched in sweat. Oh, what a nuisance, she thought. Why do I keep on having these horrible dreams, over and over? I have such a hard time sleeping!

The dreams always centered on the most frightening time she had lived through — the first days of September, the first days of war.

****

The train made very little progress in the next few days. It seemed as though all they saw were dozens of trains going in the opposite direction full of Russian troops. They could be heard singing in the distance where they bivouacked. Some of them would wave and shout to the groups who were sitting in the doorways of the parked train or walking outside. Jan Wozniak was convinced they were on the outskirts of Moscow. The friendly guard was taken off duty to the chagrin of everybody who knew him.

Wozniak, particularly, was angry that his watch was gone for just a few small favors. He began romancing the new guard assigned to their car but had very little success. He was sullen and unfriendly, and Wozniak didn't want to push his luck. Vita was relieved no end that the guard's transfer had happened after she and Ellie were safe with their new "family."

Wozniak had outlined a daily routine for his friends in the car, and, whether the train was at a standstill or moving, they all followed the instructions posted on the partition behind the mound of wood. This morning the women and girls were busy "bathing," washing their hair, and generally cleaning their half of the train car.

"Mother, may I have your scissors?" Ellie asked. "Anya is going to cut my hair off! I can't stand it any longer."

Vita quickly handed the girl a pair of sharp scissors and within the next few minutes the two long braids were off, leaving jagged edges all around her head. The girls were giggling, making fun of the uneven cutting job.

"Oh, now just a minute." Vita took charge. She snipped the hacked-up hair as well as she could, ending up with a boyish cut — very short and easy to manage.

"There, that's quite nice, Ellie." With that Ellie burst into tears.

The car, all cleaned up and everybody "bathed," the children were now organized by Jan Wozniak who every morning and afternoon would conduct "school" sessions. He had the children tell him what subjects they all had in their respective schools and what progress they had made and then he took it from there. His lectures were fascinating. He knew how to hold the children's attention for hours at a time. Vita marveled at his patience and know-how. When she told him that, he just smiled and said, "After all, I am a teacher."

The biggest effort was spent on learning Russian and that included everybody. Even the Jewish doctor and a couple of other passengers asked if they could join the Russian lessons, and soon Jan had the whole group building their vocabularies, learning pronunciations, constructing sentences, and familiarizing themselves with the strange Russian alphabet, which was neither Slavic, Latin nor Greek. Why would a P be an R, and a C be an S, and a B be a V, and the turned around backwards capital R be pronounced Ya? Ellie couldn't get over how this peculiar language looked once put down on paper.

"It sounds almost like Polish, but when you write it down, it's gibberish," she would say. She had by then been speaking French, German and quite a bit of Polish; this, though, was a horse of a different color!

Jan Wozniak procured a Russian newspaper once in a while. It was either PRAVDA or IZVIESTIA. The guards would read them and then carefully save every page to use for rolling their cigarettes. Vita, quite a heavy smoker most of her adult life, missed her cigarettes more than she liked to admit, so when Wozniak would come back from his excursions to chat with the guards and bring a newspaper and a pouch of tobacco, her eyes would light up!

"Never mind the reading lessons — let's smoke it!" she would say.

She became quite proficient in rolling a cigarette with the heavy newspaper, moistening the end flap to make it adhere to the rest of the roll. This accomplished, she would light the thicker end and puff on it contentedly.

The Russian language lessons became quite popular and almost everyone wanted to participate, with the exception of Mrs. Karowska who spoke it fluently. And old Mr. Kos who hated it and didn't want to learn it in spite of the whole group's explanations that it really was to his own advantage to know the language. Who knew how long this detention was going to last and, besides, it was good therapy. There was really nothing else to do once the daily chores were out of the way.

The "school" was divided into two groups — adults and children. Vita knew quite a bit of Russian already, so she was excused until such time as the rest of the group would catch up with her, then she would join in. She had another urgent project right now — she was sewing up a storm. She cut up one old army blanket and made it into warm vests for the Czerny children and skull caps that resembled pilot's hats for the girls. She knitted a sock-like, warm hat for Jerzy and made mittens for everyone who needed a pair. She was quite proficient with the needle and thread and soon became the official seamstress for the group.

One morning Jan leaned out of the window to check on the weather. It had been raining and sleeting for the past few days. He became very excited and shouted to the rest of them.

"Hey, our guard is back!"

When the door opened, the familiar, kind face of the Russian soldier appeared — to everyone's delight. He was also very happy to be back. It seemed that the first two or three cars of the train had some problems and extra help was needed to reinforce the guard crew. He was now back for the duration of the trip, he hoped. Wozniak joined him down on the platform. They walked off a distance and were deep in conversation when the breakfast truck arrived. When the meal was distributed, Wozniak told the group that they were indeed just a few kilometers from Moscow and that the train would pass through the city during the night, without any stops, and then proceed north to Vologda. That was all the guard knew for the time being, but he ventured a guess that the ultimate destination of the train was Siberia. Most of the labor camps were located there. He knew because his brother was sent up for two years for some small insubordination and ended up in a hard labor camp near Sura. He felt sorry for all the people on the train, but he was afraid that this was to be their lot.

Wozniak returned to the car with a long face and a dejected expression. He repeated the news to the others, sparing the children, and a general feeling of despair and gloom settled on them. They sat around the stove in a tight group and discussed their predicament. Old Mr. Kos was furious.

"This is an outrage! After all, one does not do that sort of thing in the twentieth century. Who the hell do the Russians think they are treating decent, law-abiding people this way? What right do they have to forcibly remove us from our homes and ship us off to labor camps? Is everybody going to sit here and take it?" he demanded. "What are you, slaves? Can't you do something?" He deplored his age. "If I were only a young man...."

Wozniak tried to calm him.

"Mr. Kos, you would probably get yourself shot like that other boy, remember? Don't you see? We are helpless at this moment; we have our families to think about, the children. What would happen to them if we decided to rebel right now? What we have to do is keep our wits about us — use our heads and try to stay alive and as healthy as we can."

Kos was so agitated he shook all over. He could hardly hold on to the cup of tea Vita handed him. The poor old man finally capitulated. He sadly lowered his face into the crook of his elbow and, leaning on his wife's shoulder, cried quietly. Two or three of the women wiped tears off their cheeks. Wozniak finally gave Vita a despairing look and she took the cue.

"I am really surprised at you," she said in a stern voice. "What Mr. Wozniak is telling you is the only thing we can do now. Hang on, do our best to keep going. Who knows, maybe this is just a rumor the guard has overheard. You are crying over something unknown. Save your tears for when you'll really need them. And, for God's sake, don't upset the children; they don't need to worry. So let's pull ourselves together because here they come."

The children came in from their outing ready for breakfast. It was interesting to see that the grits they formerly sneered at, now disappeared from their bowls rapidly. This morning it happened to be polenta, one of the favorite kashas served by the army field kitchen. Fortunately, there was always plenty for everybody and some of the children asked for more. Vita smiled as she watched the girls put away second bowls of polenta and wash them down with gulps of tea. They looked quite healthy considering the kind of life they led, their cheeks still pink from the calisthenics they tried to do twice daily. The nice guard allowed them to play tag in the vicinity of their car when the train was laid up. He knew it was quite safe. With the parents on board, the children would not stray too far.

Vita pushed aside the nagging thoughts about Siberia. She didn't even know what that meant, except that it would be much colder there. It might not happen, she kept assuring herself. Right now, it's one day at a time! Her thoughts were interrupted when a loud argument broke out on the opposite side of the car. It was the doctor arguing with two other men. There must be something in the air, thought Vita. Everybody is so edgy.

"You lazy fool," the doctor was yelling. "I told you hundreds of times, if this man has to go to the bathroom, you are to help him. If he is too weak to stand up, you are to hold him up. Do you understand? Look at him!"

He pointed at an old man who sat crouched in a corner of his bunk. He was thin beyond belief, his eyes sunken in his face, his lips bluish and parched. He was terribly dehydrated. The doctor said there was nothing he could do for him. The diarrhea he suffered from depleted his body of all fluids, and whenever he drank something it wouldn't stay down. The doctor explained that with infusions he would probably survive but, this way, death was just around the corner. The old man was alone. No family, no one to care for him. The man the doctor assigned to him did not want to nurse him, or clean him, or feed him. He did not care. So the poor old soul lay there in his own excrement, too weak to move and too timid to ask for help. The doctor was raging.

"I am ashamed of you. Doesn't anybody care?"

Several voices finally were raised and they were all shouting.

"If you care so much, why don't you clean him up? You have a big mouth; all you do is criticize us. How about you? Or your precious wife over there? Let her clean the shit — or is she better than us?"

It would have probably come to blows if the big sliding door hadn't opened and two guards appeared in the opening.

"What's going on here?" they demanded.

Wozniak explained that one old man was very ill and that if something weren't done for him he would die within a couple of days. He belonged in a hospital. Couldn't they do something about it? They promised to report it to the train commandant. He was in charge of this transport. Tovarish Sergey Gregorovich, member of the NKVD, rank, Major in the Soviet Army. Wozniak was curious about him. He made a mental note to find out why a high-ranking officer would be put in charge of a train full of civilians headed for a labor camp. He must ask the guard about him. In the meantime though, there were other, more important things to take care of. Dr. Helman wasn't welcome among the Jews anymore. There was open hostility between the passengers and the doctor's family. Wozniak walked over to the other side of the car and saw Dr. Helman struggle alone to clean the old man up. He decided to give him a hand. Together they stripped the foul clothing off the man and tenderly gave him a sponge bath. They then wrapped him in a clean sheet and moved him close to the "hole." They bundled up the man's clothing and bedding in an old blanket and set it aside to dispose of later when the train would start moving again. The rest of the angry passengers sat motionless, glaring at the two men at their work. Nobody made a move to help. The doctor's wife was crying loudly, holding their two small children in her arms. Wozniak brewed up some tea and tried to pour it into the old man's mouth, with little success.

"He will go," the doctor said, raising the man's eyelids with his thumb, "if he doesn't keep this tea down. He is just too dehydrated."

Presently the guard was back. He called Wozniak out of the car and told him that the old man would be removed from the train as soon as an ambulance could be brought over. Wozniak was relieved. They might be able to do something for him at the hospital, he thought. He came back and told the doctor and the others about the news.

Marta Kucharska now took over from the doctor and tried to make the old man swallow some liquids. His mouth hung open and the liquid oozed out down his chin, as soon as it was poured in. Then he choked and threw up the few drops that she managed to make him swallow. It was almost dark when a car pulled up to the train. It was a military lorry with a canvas top and two stretchers mounted in the rear. Two attendants got out of the cab and the guard directed them to the proper door. They quickly hopped on, rolled the old man in a blanket, put him on a stretcher and took him out. He never moved.

Wozniak gathered his group of passengers and suggested that they ask the doctor and his family to move over to their side of the car. He felt that Dr. Helman would be an asset to have among them. He very shrewdly explained that it would really be wise in the long run to have a doctor available, who was a friend and who was somewhat obligated to them for this extension of friendship.

The only opposition came from Mrs. Karowska who thought the idea absurd. She was not about to fraternize with any Jew — doctor or not. The majority felt Jan was right, and Vita and Jan were selected to go over and extend the invitation. Vita felt very much like Mrs. Karowska, but reason won out. Observing the man, she formed an immediate opinion based upon his kindness to the dying old man and the gentle consideration he had given his wife who was obviously detached from reality. Helman was of medium height, slight built, with large gentle dark eyes, framed by heavy-rimmed glasses and an ascetic face. She knew very well what Jan's proposal could mean to all of them in case of some unforeseen illness or accident. So, the two of them approached the doctor.

"Dr. Helman," Jan said, "we thought perhaps you would be more comfortable if you joined our group. We would like you and your family to move over for the rest of the journey."

Dr. Helman was much obliged. He thanked them and immediately started putting his things together. He glanced at his wife and took Jan aside.

"She is not well. She is very unstable mentally. As a matter of fact, we just brought her home from a sanatorium a few days before the war broke out. I am afraid this situation has set her back beyond repair. I can't get through to her."

They felt sorry for him. At best, this was a terrible ordeal, but to have to worry about this sort of illness in these conditions was unbearable.

It didn't take long to move the family over and settle them next to Mr. and Mrs. Kos. They were kind, old people and made every effort to make the doctor and his family as welcome as they could.

No sooner had they settled down, another fight erupted among the Jews. They were screaming at each other and several of them engaged in fisticuffs. Dr. Helman explained; from what he could make out, they were fighting over the sick, old man's possessions. Somebody said that he was very wealthy and had a lot of valuables with him. They were ripping his clothing apart and searching through his bundles to find the cached treasures.

"Animals!" was all the doctor could manage to say. "I am ashamed of them."

"Oh, don't feel that way," said Jan. "This is just human nature. Some of us are greedier than others. Here comes supper!" Then the friendly guard was at the door, smiling and waving to Jan to come closer. Wozniak moved over and was told that the old man arrived safely at the local hospital and was well taken care of. This news made everyone feel much better. Soon everything fell back into the regular nightly routine and the incident was quickly forgotten.

****

The train was steadily moving north. Moscow was far behind and the countryside was changing quite markedly. Spring was apparently just around the corner because the days were longer and sunny and slight traces of green could be seen around the trees and bushes. The buds were beginning to pop. Some of the land under till was ready to be worked.

"Isn't it amazing how much open, uninhabited space there is?" Wozniak said to the passengers, peering through the slightly opened door as the train rattled along. "No wonder they need extra hands."

Sometimes for miles and miles they would see nothing but dense forests with no sign of habitation, no railroad stations, no roads, just one lonely track going somewhere. They all wondered where.

The train was on the move with few interruptions, the country being virtually unpopulated. This was reflected in the way the prisoners were served their meals. They were sporadic, late and sometimes totally absent. Most of the food supplies the families had with them were long gone. The train kitchen did its best, but with no new provisions, there was very little to prepare. The kasha was runny, the soup watery, and there was no bread at all. Wozniak complained to the guards, but all they said was, "Soon we will get to a city and there will be food."

There were many nights when the children were given small rations of whatever was available, and the grownups went to bed hungry.

The guard came over one evening when the train was pulled over on a side track for the night. He and Jan had their usual friendly talk. He told Jan that this train was indeed going to Vologda, a city on a direct line to Archangelsk. He did not know whether they would proceed any further, but he said he knew of several hard labor camps located in the vicinity of Vologda and northeast of the city along the Suchona River. He described the climate and the desolate country to Jan who felt cold shivers down his spine, trying to picture his family and friends surviving in that sort of place. He decided to keep most of the information to himself. He would tell the group only the important news, there was no point upsetting them with speculations.

****

On March 24th, 1940, the train pulled into the town of Vologda. It was quite strange to see a large city after miles and miles of woods and just an occasional kolhos (communal government farm) where the land had been cleared for agriculture. These kolhoses were clustered around the rail line, which was used to ship out their produce and bring up supplies during the long winters.

Vologda was a pretty town, well populated, full of trees and quite hilly. From where the train was situated on the outskirts, on an isolated track, one could see a portion of the downtown area and some outlying streets. On one of the higher points, there stood a splendid Orthodox church with several gold, round cupolas glistening in the sun.

Vita and Ellie were sitting on the platform railing getting a little air and sun. It was such a treat to be outside. Wozniak came running up to them; he was obviously excited.

"Listen, there is something afoot! I heard some of the guards say that this is it, that we will be taken off the train. I couldn't find our guard anywhere to confirm this, but I know something is happening. They are not loading any supplies and the Commandant and his two aides went into town. They have never done this before, not even in Moscow!"

When they returned to their car, they noticed that the news had already reached some of the passengers. A general unrest could be felt, the sort of unrest that comes with a feeling of anxiety based on not knowing what will happen next, a feeling that twists the gut and steps up the pulse.

"Does anybody have a cigarette?" inquired Vita.

Stan Kucharski sat down next to her and rolled two cigarettes out of a newspaper and tobacco he had managed to save. She thanked him and took several hard pulls, inhaling the smoke slowly and deliberately. It seemed to calm her.

"Does anybody have any details? What next?" she asked.

They all shook their heads. All they had heard was that the train was not going any further. What would happen to the passengers, nobody knew. Wozniak was somewhere looking for their guard. He did not return until almost dinner time and would not discuss the matter, he said, not until after the meal. The food finally came — barley soup, a slice of white bread, called cake by the Russians, and "tea." A virtual feast!

After the dinner things were all cleared away, the group gathered in a tight circle and Jan shared the news he had obtained from his friend. This was definitely the end of the train journey. They were to stay on it until arrangements were made with the local army garrison for transport from the train to the Suchona River, he believed, and the next leg of the journey was to be made by some kind of boat or barge. Several hard-labor campsites were located north of there and one of them could be designated for this group. The sites were quite far apart. Some of them were farm kolhoses, others timber labor camps. It was anybody's guess where they would land. Wozniak stressed that it was very important that they all stick together. As a group they could help each other — particularly the women and children. He spread open the makeshift map and drew a line up north from Moscow, marked Vologda at the end of the line and wrote: "Appr. 400 Klms." Then he added the date at that point: "March 24, 1940."

"Six weeks!" Vita said. "Imagine, we have been on this train for six weeks!"

She moved over to the bench where most of the children were sitting in a tight group and, sensing the anxiety in their parents, they were all quiet and frightened.

"We hear that we are to be moved onto a boat pretty soon. Won't it be nice to be out in the sun during the day and get rid of some of this prison pallor?" she asked.

"Oh, yuk!" said Ellie. "I will probably be seasick as soon as I get on it!"

"It's a river, silly. Who ever heard of anybody getting seasick on a river?"

"Oh, Mother, you know me. I'll manage!"

Vita had to laugh although the girl was right. Every trip they had ever taken on any kind of boat, large or small, on the sea or lake, Ellie suffered from mal de mer more than anybody she had ever known.

Jan decided not to hold any classes that evening; nobody could concentrate. They were all wondering what tomorrow would bring. So they just sat around, talking in low voices about the past, the times before the war, their loved ones left behind, and about tomorrow.

"There is no use speculating," Jan kept repeating, "tomorrow will come soon enough."

Finally they all turned in. Sleep came to some almost instantly. Their even breathing could be heard and an occasional snore here and there. I wish to God I could sleep that way, Vita thought. It would be a blessing to be able to close my eyes and not know or feel anything for a few hours. She wanted a cigarette in the worst way, but the strict rule was: absolutely no smoking in the straw bunks, so she just stared into space trying not to move for fear of waking Ellie who was curled up close to her. Somebody was still up — she could hear some movement near the stove and a few whispers now and then. She strained to see who it was when a few flickers in the dying embers lit up the area for a second or two. It was Jan Wozniak sitting very close to Anya Karowska with his arm around her shoulders. Then she could see their faces in the glow of the embers. He was whispering something to her, his lips close to her ear, her face spellbound....

What on earth? Why, that old lecher! Vita was beside herself. It seemed incredible that a man of his age, a man she respected so much, would behave like this right under his own wife's nose, at a time like this! What was the matter with him? Her first reaction was to get up and let them know she was aware of their little tryst, but then she thought of the consequences, and maybe she was jumping to conclusions. Maybe this was nothing. She started to cough; there was a rapid movement and next thing she could make out was Jan standing over the stove trying to rekindle the fire. Anya was gone. Vita slid out of her bunk and wrapped a blanket over her shoulders. She carefully made her way down to the floor and over to the stove.

"Hello," she said. "Having trouble sleeping? I didn't close an eye all night!"

"You are not the only one," replied Jan evenly. "All this time I have been up; there has been somebody keeping me company, off and on. Everybody is restless. Can you blame them?"

She looked at him suspiciously, then she felt ashamed of herself. He was as calm as ever, his thin, handsome face composed, a gentle smile in his eyes.

"I bet you would like a cigarette?" he asked.

Vita nodded, and he proceeded to roll one for her and one for himself. She decided to ignore the incident she had witnessed and give Jan the benefit of the doubt. She promised herself, though, to keep a watchful eye on the two.

They smoked in silence for a while, then Jan stood up, stretched his arms and said, "Well, I think I will try to catch some sleep. I advise you to do the same. Remember, you and I are the strongest people in the whole bunch. I depend on you."

With these words, he bent over and planted a light kiss on Vita's forehead and was gone. The gesture was so unexpected and happened so fast it caught her completely off guard. She was stunned.

Oh, this man is clever, she thought. He depends on me, is that what he said, he depends on me? As much as she liked and admired him, he now made her angry. His tactics reminded her of a chess game. Your move, Vita Kew!

She didn't remember how long she sat on the bench, but she must have nodded off for a while because when she came to, the fire was out and it was dawning outside. Stiff and achy, she got up to her bunk to wait for tomorrow.

****

March 25, 1940. There was little room on the small calendar pages Vita was filling with her notes and comments. Wozniak traded a pair of her earrings for a couple of pencils, a bottle of ink for her fountain pen and some scratch paper. The nice guard walked over to town to get the items and also brought a map of the USSR. Wozniak was delighted. He would study it by the hour, comparing his makeshift drawing with the real thing.

They were indeed on the banks of the Suchona River, which looked as if it were flowing toward a town called Kotlas, where it joined the Divina River which, in turn, flowed all the way up to Archangelsk and into the White Sea. He wondered just how far they would go. Siberia? Just the thought of that vast, cold, cursed land gripped him with fear. There was such a ring of finality connected with that word — "Siberia." Once you were banished there, you were done for. Finished! He thought of his two little daughters. How would they ever survive?

"Mr. Wozniak," Vita was tapping his shoulder, "the guard wants to talk to you."

He looked up at her, startled.

"Are you all right?" she asked, seeing his troubled face.

"Yes, yes, I am fine. Tell him I will be right there."

He pulled himself together, folded his new map and all his papers neatly, put them away and hopped off the train. When he came back, he carried a tin bucket filled with something resembling sour cream.

"It's kefir," he explained. "It's supposed to be very good, just like yogurt. It's from our guard. Sort of a farewell gift!"

It was quickly dished up for the entire group and consumed with obvious pleasure. It did taste like yogurt, but was much sweeter and thicker.

Wozniak then relayed some of the news he had obtained from the guard. Early next morning all the prisoners were to be transferred onto several barges and shipped up the Suchona River to their next destination.

"Where? How far?" they all wanted to know.

"I wish I could answer that. The guard did not know. He is going back with the train," Wozniak explained.

He was not going to go any further with his own speculations. They would find out soon enough.

****

At six a.m. the transfer began. The first cars of the train were emptied and people herded in a long line across several tracks to a clearing, and from there down the wide bank to the edge of the river. The friendly guard came running to Wozniak to tell him to take their time getting ready. The first group was going down below into the barges where conditions were much worse than on the top deck.

"Stay back as long as you can. I will come to get you when the time is right," he said and ran off.

When he came back, he carried a large sack of suharki — dried chunks of bread, hard, black, resembling huge croutons.

"The food will be awful; these might help. And don't drink the water unless you boil it. They take it from the river."

And then he was gone.

They were herded up a narrow plank to the top deck of an enormous flat barge, normally used to transport lumber. There must have been five hundred people being crowded onto the barge.

"There is some space in the bow," they were instructed as they inched their way through a narrow passage, stepping over people, bedding, belongings; being cursed at by the ones already sprawled on the deck.

They found a small area next to a large smoke stack and dropped their bundles onto the deck, exhausted and bewildered. There was so little space left on that part of the deck that lying down for the night was out of the question. All they could do was sit, propped up against the stack, hoping the trip would be mercifully short. But that was not to be. When they finally got underway, they questioned the wisdom of choosing the upper deck. The bone-chilling wind blew from the port side, spraying the huddling bodies with fine, freezing mist. The blankets they were covered with were getting wet and half frozen. Wozniak pushed through the crowds to find some official to complain about the crowded conditions, the lack of protection from the elements, and to demand hot water for the children, but when he found one of the barge's crew members, he was laughed at and told that all first class accommodations were taken. It was about time the capitalists found out how the common folk lived!

The barges moved up the river until dusk when they finally pulled over to the edge and anchored there for the night. There was a small pier with a few people milling about, setting down a row of buckets filled with something resembling gray, watery soup. Wozniak and Vita distributed the croutons to their group. The swill in the buckets was not fit for human consumption. Dr. Helman somehow got a container of boiled water and that was their day's meal. The stack they were huddled against was now warm, so they took turns warming their bodies, trying to dry out their clothing. The warm train car with its lumpy, straw-covered shelves seemed, by comparison, an enviable accommodation.

Vita was fuming. "This is criminal! I am not going to stand for it! There has to be a captain on the barge, and he is going to hear from me!"

"Mrs. Kew, it won't do you any good," both Helman and Wozniak tried to convince her. "The captain has orders to get these people from point A to point B, and that is all he is interested in. He doesn't give a damn how uncomfortable you are. You will just anger him. Please, calm down. We will somehow survive these few days."

She was close to tears, angry and frustrated and, above all, helpless.

They got under way again very early the next morning. At this point, the river was quite a bit wider with some traffic going in the opposite direction. The day was sunny and the wind had died down, making it a little more bearable. The most humiliating thing was the bathroom routine. The few areas provided for that daily, bodily function were virtually inaccessible with the hundreds of people using them and, if by chance, one could get in, they were so filthy it was impossible to even step inside over the mounds of excrement piled on the flooring. After inspecting the "facility" with her own eyes, Vita returned to the group in total despair. Just the thought of that place made her gag repeatedly. It was such an assault on human dignity, she couldn't bear it. For the first time during the ordeal, she felt herself unhinging. This was not happening to her, it was not real; any minute she would wake up and find herself back home in her beautiful, clean bed. Paul and Ellie would be there. She felt her daughter's arms around her, squeezing, shaking her.

"Mother, please don't cry. It'll be all right. We don't have to go there; we have a system!"

"A system? What system?" Vita wiped her face, looking up at Ellie incredulously.

"You will see. Dr. Helman and I invented it! We will hold up a blanket for privacy, use that tin bucket the guard brought us, and then dump the stuff in the river! Well?"

Oh, God, thought Vita. She pulled herself together. Her friends were eyeing her anxiously.

"Well, Ellie, let's try your invention right now!"

****

The group around the stack was getting ready to spend another night, taking turns resting in a half-prone position, then sitting up the rest of the night to let others stretch a bit. How much longer? Patience was wearing thin; arguments broke out here and there; children could be heard crying for hours on end. The evening meal was a gray, watery soup with dried fish pieces swimming here and there. Most of the group dumped the swill overboard and munched on the croutons, washing them down with hot water that Dr. Helman somehow obtained twice a day.

****

"Is there a doctor here? Please, we need a doctor," somebody was calling.

"Yes, over here, I am a doctor," Helman answered.

The man inched his way down the deck, stepping over sleeping forms.

"Please doctor, it's my daughter. She has had a terrible bellyache for the last two days, has been vomiting, and now we can't wake her up. Can you help us? Please?"

The man was haggard, dirty and desperate. Dr. Helman followed him to the other side of the barge and was gone for a long time. When he returned, he just shook his head.

"It's too late. Peritonitis. The poor child must have suffered terribly. She is now unconscious. Won't last the night."

"Were you able to find anybody in charge of this stinking boat?" asked Wozniak.

"Yes, but they have no facilities of any kind, not even a spare bunk! The captain told me Kotlas was not too far up the river. We should reach it sometime tomorrow, and then go on further north up the Divina River to some campsite. He did not know where. It will probably take another day."

Wozniak had to wait till morning to check his map. Another day! He rebelled inwardly.

****

Vita made few notations in her little calendar. She used words she had not realized were in her vocabulary. If this ever gets into their hands, I am dead, she thought, slipping her writing things behind a piece of torn lining in her suitcase.

****

The barges finally came to an area where the river was too narrow and shallow to navigate. They were to get off early next morning.

The unloading took forever. There were several barges anchored alongside, all filled beyond capacity. A new cadre of armed soldiers took charge now, shouting orders, grouping the crowds into segments of approximately 100 heads and leading each to a long hut to register. Each prisoner was then given a portion of bread and a piece of dried, smoked fish.

"Stay close together," admonished Wozniak, herding his friends, helping with their bundles, carrying the small children. Stan Kucharski and the doctor also had their hands full. Vita, weak and stiff, was barely able to manage. Ellie carried most of their belongings, leaving the heaviest behind.

The next leg of the journey was to be made on foot. There was still a lot of snow on the ground; it was cold, but mercifully there was no wind.

"Here, follow us," shouted the two guards at the head of the line. There was a curious road leading into the woods. Two narrow, wooden lanes, each as wide as a large truck's wheels, were elevated off the ground about a foot or more by wooden ties. Two large logs split into halves and laid side by side formed the base of each lane and were curbed on either side by logs to prevent vehicles from slipping off into the bog. The flat portion of the path was about two feet wide, the two logs framing it were at least a foot higher, so if a vehicle of sorts got on these two "rails," it had to travel on them until the end. These "rails" also provided paths wide enough to walk on.

Two long lines formed behind each guard and followed him at a slow pace.

"How far do we have to go? There are small children, sick and old people here," some of the people shouted at the guards.

One of them stopped, turned to face the prisoners and said, "It is just a few kilometers into the woods. If any of you can't make it, step off the road and sit in the snow until the next group comes along."

Vita's group struggled on. The men took turns carrying the small children piggyback. Ellie dragged her largest bundle behind her. Vita carried her suitcase, her bag and a couple of blankets draped over her shoulders. She was hungry, tired and very angry. Ellie, walking in front of her, kept glancing back to check on her mother and all the others. The lines were dwindling quite a bit. Some of the old Jews, too weak to continue, were getting off and sitting down in the snow to rest. The pace kept getting slower and slower. The two front guards were quite a distance ahead of the prisoners when the leaders of the two lines simply refused to go any further. They sat down on the logs and all the others followed.

"Okay," yelled the guards. "Ten minutes. That's all!"

They barely had a chance to sit down when, at the end of the road, coming out of a bend, they could hear and see a large truck making its way down the rails, spewing black smoke from the two cylinders mounted on each side of the cab. The cylinders contained water that was heated over two birch log fires.

"Everybody off! Let him pass!" yelled the guard.

The prisoners scrambled off their perches and slid into the knee-deep snow on either side of the road. The truck hauled a load of timber. As it chugged by on its rails, the two cab occupants waved to the prisoners. Wozniak walked up to the guards and spoke with them for a few minutes. He was shaking his head when he came back.

"It's still quite a few kilometers to the campsite. We simply have to make an effort to get there, otherwise we will have to spend the night right here on the road."

"Look," Mr. Kos was now shouting. "They have trucks running up and down this road. Why can't they use those to transport the people? I just can't walk any further."

"Please try," pleaded Wozniak. "Hang on to me. I don't want to leave you behind."

And so they marched on. Finally, almost at dusk, they came to a clearing in the dense woods and saw long rows of log buildings.

****

13

CAMP VOZEMKA

Spring 1940.
Finland capitulated to Russia.
Germany seized Denmark, Norway and Belgium.
In the Katyn Forest 4,000 Polish officers and 11,000 soldiers
who had surrendered, were massacred by the Russians,
who led the world to believe it had been done by the Germans.

"This is Camp Vozemka," announced the guard. "Wait here, don't move. We will report to the commandant and then get you something to eat."

The guards marched up to a small cabin and rapped on the door. A man in uniform came out, looked the new arrivals over and gave some instructions, pointing in the direction of several buildings, and then went back in. One of the guards walked over to a larger, square building, the other joined the group.

"There will be food ready for you in a few minutes; right now, you there," he pointed to Wozniak, "divide them into groups of twenty, and we will get you assigned to your quarters!"

There were approximately 75 or 78 left out of the original group of a hundred. The others must have stayed behind. Wozniak moved his friends into a close group and quickly counted the others, assembling them in small clusters of the required number.

News evidently spread through the barracks that a new transport of prisoners had arrived and many men and women came running out.

"Where are you from? Anybody from Lvov? Is there a Katz family here? What's happening in Poland? Is the war still on?"

They were starved for any scrap of information they could get. The guards were back now, pushing them away and ordering them to return to their barracks. Wozniak had his group all ready to be assigned to some shelter. They followed the soldier to a building that had a narrow hallway with doors at either end, and a row of rooms approximately twelve feet by twelve feet in size.

"Take four rooms for this group," ordered the guard.

"Mrs. Kew," said Wozniak. "You and Ellie take Nella and Dorotka; the Kucharskis and Jerzy can go into the middle room; Mrs. Karowska and we will take the next one and the Koses and Helmans can have the last one. All right?"

They carried their belongings into the rooms, looking around at the dirty floor, stained log walls, one small window and a stone "piechka," a wood-burning stove with a two-hole cook top.

"I want to see the commandant," demanded Wozniak. "This is an outrage! There is no place to sleep, or sit down...."

"Shut up!" The guard raised his fist up to Wozniak's face. "All you do is bitch. I have had enough. You will get your beds tomorrow, so shut your mouth and get your ass to the kitchen for your food!"

They got their bowls and cups out and marched out behind Wozniak heading toward the kitchen. A long line had already formed in front of a counter, behind which two people were serving portions of kasha with a small teaspoon of oil in the center of it, a slice of black bread and "kipiatok" (hot water) out of a large samovar. Apparently this was the regular evening meal served to all the internees. It was welcome, though, because it was hot and filling.

Back in their rooms, Jerzy and Ellie started a fire in the piechka. There were piles of split wood outside the barracks and the children carried in enough to keep the fire going all night. Jerzy's small hunting knife came in handy to cut slivers of wood and strip chunks of birch bark for kindling. Soon a fire was burning brightly, lighting up the dismal room.

"Here, children, spread the blankets on the floor in front of the stove and put some of the extra clothing on top. It will have to do until tomorrow," said Vita.

The room warmed up almost immediately, and the children settled down on their ragged palettes. Dorotka cried pitifully hugging her doll.

"I want to go home," she kept saying over and over. "Where is my mama?"

"She is in heaven," whispered her sister.

It made Vita's heart break to hear the two small orphans. What injustice, what fate. What kind of future did these children have? She was so tired and emotionally spent, but she couldn't sleep. She sat up most of the night feeding the fire in the stove and watching over the children.

At six o'clock in the morning the barracks came to life. Vita could hear loud voices up and down the little hallway, and finally a knock on the door and Wozniak's voice: "Mrs. Kew, are you up? May I come in?"

Ellie jumped up from her pad and lifted the crude latch on the door. Wozniak came in, carrying a large steaming teapot.

"Good morning. Here is some kipiatok. Have you been able to rest a little?"

"Well, the children slept most of the night. What's the plan for today? Oh, and where is the bathroom?"

"At eight o'clock there is supposed to be a meeting of all the new arrivals. The commandant wants to 'greet' us personally! The latrines are behind this building. They are quite busy right now, but by seven o'clock, when the work day starts around here, it will be easier to get in."

"What do you think we will do here?" asked Vita, filling the children's' cups with hot water.

"We will find out soon enough. I will pick you up when it's time to go. They want us to assemble on time!"

****

The meeting room was a part of the kitchen building. There were several rows of benches in front of the room, the rest of the space was standing room. Vita and the other women and children of Wozniak's group sat down on the last row of benches with the men standing behind them. The commandant and one armed soldier marched in at exactly eight o'clock.

"Zdrastfujtie tovarishs," he greeted them. There was total silence.

"I am Comrade Igor Ivanovitch Smolensky. I am in charge of this camp. We are engaged in productive effort here to aid the USSR. I will expect one hundred percent effort out of every able man and woman. Laziness will not be tolerated. You will be fed according to your productivity. I am sure you read the sign posted out there. HTO NYE ROBOTAYET, TOT NYE KUSHAYET. And we mean exactly that! You don't work, you don't eat! We are in the process of building new houses, and most of you will be assigned to help with that work. After that is finished, the Soviet Union needs lumber. You will be divided into groups and assigned work in the woods. Work starts at six a.m. in the summer and at seven a.m. in the winter. Tools will be provided as needed. You will be fed at noon and in the evening. And, again, the better you work, the more food you will get. There are two large bath houses, one at each end of the camp. I urge you to use them. They will be off limits between four and six p.m. Those hours are set aside for the camp officials."

He went on and on, standing there, his hands behind his back, his legs spread apart. He was of medium height, slight build, with light brown hair, cut very short, blue piercing eyes and a permanent scowl, giving his rather handsome face a hard, no-nonsense expression.

"We will be meeting here once a week, after supper. Everyone has to attend. No other meetings of groups larger than three will be permitted anywhere. And don't even think of leaving the camp without permission. Punishment for insubordination will be severe. I run this camp efficiently and fairly. If you have any questions, I will be glad to answer them."

"Comrade...." Wozniak lifted his hand.

"Not now!" snapped the soldier, standing at the commandant's side.

"As I was saying," continued Igor Ivanovitch, his scowl deepening, "you follow the rules and you will do fine."

With that, he marched out of the room without even a glance at the people. Two new officials took over the meeting. One of them talked at length about the great soviet soyuze, its size, its power, its accomplishments. When he was finished, the other one stepped forward and announced: "We will now learn a song. Pay attention because we will be singing it at our next meeting."

He sang the first verse: "Polushko, pole, polushko shiroko pole."

They exchanged astonished glances, but Wozniak kept nodding his head, encouraging them to follow orders. He particularly kept glaring at Mr. Kos, who absolutely refused to participate.

The meeting was finally over and they returned to their rooms.

A crudely built rope cot and a mattress ticking were all the amenities offered to each of the internees. The cots were stored outside, piled high in a heap. Wozniak picked them over, handing the most decent-looking ones to Stan Kucharski. They then had to be "disinfected" by dipping them in a huge tank of boiling water, heated by a log fire under it. The men dunked each cot in the steaming water, first one end then the other, then tossed them in the snow to drip dry.

"What are you doing?" Vita wanted to know.

Dr. Helman explained that this was a very primitive, but quite effective way to clean the cots of bed bugs and anything else the previous user....

"Don't go into any details," Vita interrupted. "I would just as soon not know!"

She had been busy stuffing mattress-ticking with straw, trying to pick out bunches that looked dry and fresh. An official directed the activities. He told them they had just a couple of days to get settled.

"Then you go to work," he announced. "We are building additional housing and you will help with that."

He also told the men that they could use the scrap lumber at the construction site to build whatever they needed.

With the cots all boiled and drying, the men concentrated on building "furniture." Here, Stan Kucharski showed his talents. Under his watchful eye, pieces of discarded flooring boards were measured, cut and assembled. Ellie and Anya worked together pounding nails, at first not too successfully, but finally getting somewhat proficient.

"What else do you want me to build, Mother," asked Ellie, showing off a bench she had just nailed together.

"Oh, now let's see. How about a piano?"

"Mother, be serious. Would you like a shelf? Mr. Kucharski built two of them. I can make one for us."

"That would be very nice."

Mr. Kucharski cut the boards for her, and she nailed them together, making a three-tiered shelf about three feet long and twelve inches deep. It tilted slightly to one side, but propped up against the wall, it would do fine.

Wozniak got one of the officials to bring them some buckets and scrub brushes and a container of pasty, gray, vile-smelling soap. They scrubbed the rough floor boards, washed off the grimy walls and, by dinner time, each room had one cot per person, a small table, two benches and shelves. Jerzy was in charge of the fire in their room. He never let it die, making the room unbearably hot and damp. Vita tried to open the window but found it inoperable. It was just a piece of glass in a frame, built right into the wall.

There were three people in their group not willing to participate in any of these activities: Sarah Helman, mentally detached from reality; Mrs. Karowska, claiming bad health; and old Mr. Kos, just being stubborn and contrary. Fortunately, their roommates shouldered their responsibilities and provided for them. Vita was upset by their attitude. She didn't enjoy scrubbing filthy floors and walls either, but did her share.

At dinner time, besides their portion of food, they were also given a bar of soap, a bottle of some liquid disinfectant, a wooden bowl and a wooden spoon, a kerosene lamp, a tea kettle, matches, two cooking pots, towels and a box of tooth powder. After the meal, Vita, Maria Wozniak and the girls decided to try out the bathhouse. The two bath buildings were located quite a distance from the center of the camp at the end of one cluster of barracks. There were quite a few other people going in and out of the building. Vita walked in first, wondering what the degree of privacy would be. Would it be like the latrines? Those were just long buildings, marked "Men" and "Women," but the inside was all open, one long seat with a dozen holes, one beside the other.

The girls followed Vita into a small hallway and then into the bath. The heat was intense. They peeled off their clothing and laid it on a bench which ran all along the entire wall. Quite a few women were there already, pouring water on the hot stones and sending up billows of steam. It was a large room with a slatted wood floor, dimly lit by a couple of kerosene lamps hanging from the rafters. The hot stones were piled high in three metal containers, which were heated by a roaring log fire in a stone pit. Barrels of water stood by with huge wooden dippers hanging from their sides. Vita had heard of this type of sauna bath but had never been in one. Soon the steam enveloped them and it got uncomfortably hot. Clumsily, at first, they washed and rinsed themselves off with cool water. There were long brooms made out of thin willow twigs lying around on the benches.

"You are supposed to whip yourself with these," said Maria Wozniak, apparently more familiar with this strange routine. "It's good for the circulation. Then you cool off outside in the snow."

"Oh, by all means, you go first," said Vita, rubbing Ellie and herself off with a towel.

They got their clothes on in a hurry, bundled their heads up in scarves, and ran all the way back to their barracks. The bath made them all feel much better.

"Mother, I am hungry. Is there anything left from dinner?" asked Ellie.

"You can have a piece of bread and some hot water."

She unwrapped the two slices of bread she was saving for breakfast and handed Ellie her portion. The girl roasted the bread on top of the cook stove and put their newly acquired teapot on to boil. Vita spread the blankets on the cots, trying to smooth the straw lumps down. Nella had pushed her cot close to Dorotka's so that she could easily reach the little girl to comfort her.

"Put all your dirty clothes on the floor, next to the door. We will have to get them washed somehow, somewhere," instructed Vita.

"Mrs. Kew, I only have one sweater," said Nella.

"Oh, dear! Here take one of Ellie's for now. We will have to do something about that tomorrow. Do you have any night clothes?"

"Yes, one, and Dorotka has one also. They are both clean."

"Well, from now on, use those at night only. Tomorrow put on Ellie's sweater and your ski pants and we will wash your other clothes. And Dorotka's too."

"Thank you, Mrs. Kew."

Nella changed into her nightie, folding her worn, dirty clothes and stacking them on the floor.

Vita felt sorry for the children. She imagined Ellie, all alone, among strangers in this God-forsaken place and resolved to take better care of them. Dorotka was only eight years old. She couldn't imagine why the Russians would transport children into forced labor camps...or women, for that matter. Wozniak was right in speculating that they were clearing that part of Poland of all the Poles to resettle their own people. She couldn't sleep. She extricated her little diary and her writing things out of their hiding place and, taking the lamp to the table, made as many notations as the space allowed her under the April 1st date. This certainly was a cruel April Fool's joke, she thought bitterly.

****

There was plenty of water, but the well was far away and there was usually a long line of people, buckets in hand, waiting their turn. Here the children came in handy — they took turns in the line, running in to warm up from time to time. Vita was doing the wash. Stan Kucharski brought them a large, twelve liter tin with a handle and a lid. She washed the small items first, handing them to the girls to take outside and wring them out. After they were rinsed, they spread them on the clean snow to freeze. At night they hung them in their rooms on a clothes line apparently left behind by previous occupants. Even wool pants and sweaters had to be carefully washed in cool water and freeze-dried. What a system, she thought, half-disgusted, half-amused. But it was this or live in dirty clothes. Or, she thought, she might take the smaller items to the bath house and wash them out there one by one.

As they lined up in front of the kitchen counter for their noon soup and bread, Wozniak came close to Vita and whispered to her, "Do you have a small item in your jewelry cache you can spare?"

"Oh, I have lots of things. What do you need it for?"

"Well, you know how these people love to barter. You can't bribe them with money; they can't buy anything with it, but they would do anything to get gold or stones or watches. I think I know whom to approach."

"I'll get it for you right after lunch, but be careful," warned Vita. Bribing an official was a crime, punishable by a long jail sentence. He nodded reassuringly and, collecting his barley soup, left the kitchen.

Vita sent the girls outside to gather some of the drying clothes, and she could hear them laughing as they carried the frozen sweaters, pants and underwear.

"Look, Mother, there is half a man standing there!" shouted Ellie, pointing to a pair of pants standing upright in a snow bank. She looked out the window amused by the sight, but her full attention was on her task of ripping open the lining of her purse and rummaging through the odds and ends of jewelry she had hidden there. She thought wistfully of George Dubczyk and wondered whatever had happened to him and his family. Had they been able to escape or were they also caught and sent into Russia?

She picked out a round gold lapel pin, set with small rubies and diamonds. This one was her own, but she always disliked it and she was glad she could now use it, maybe in exchange for food or some other needed items. Jan Wozniak would do his best, she was sure. He was very clever and resourceful. She put the pin in her coat pocket to pass on to him at her first opportunity.

****

Four Russians, not in uniform, were put in charge of the work assignments for the new arrivees. Every man, woman and child over fifteen years of age, was considered an adult and was required to comply with a certain standard of labor to qualify for that day's ration of food. Vita's group was led to where the new barracks were being constructed. Mrs. Kos was given the job of looking after the smaller children. Mr. Kos, because of his age and disabilities, was to help a Russian crew repairing tools and sharpening axes and saws.

There were several people at the site already, swinging axes, sawing logs, stripping off the bark, cutting deep notches at each end of the logs and lifting them up to fit one over the other to form a log wall. Mrs. Karowska, Vita and their two daughters were each given a narrow wooden wedge and a hammer and instructed to fill the spaces between the logs with some grainy, rough substance resembling glass wool, then pounding it in to fill all the gaps. A large fire burned a distance from the site. Some of the women were gathering the discarded bark, branches and small remnants of lumber and carrying their loads to the fire. The men were doing much harder work. It took three or four of the new arrivees to lift a long, heavy log and pass it up to the Russian builders who jeered and laughed at the weak city capitalists trying to do an honest day's work.

"Robotai, robotai!" they would yell at the staggering, clumsy men, almost caving in under the heavy weight. Dr. Helman protested to the supervisors, but got nowhere. He was told this was not a holiday they were on, so they had better shape up, or there would be no food tokens for their evening meal.

"My Stan is used to heavy work," said Mrs. Kucharska, working next to Vita, "but the others, the doctor, or Mr. Wozniak, how will they manage?"

"I have no idea. The whole thing is insanity," replied Vita, watching the struggling men out of the corner of her eye. Young Marian ran up and gave them a hand, and finally they lifted the log above their heads and handed it to the two Russians who easily placed it on top of the others, fitting it into the notches. A chorus of cheers followed the men's effort.

"Well, don't just stand there. Get another one!" shouted the boss.

During the mid-morning break, they all gathered by the roaring bonfire to warm their hands and feet. Vita walked over to Wozniak and slipped him the gold pin she had in her pocket.

"Okay, okay, back to work," shouted the supervisors.

The next break was at lunchtime. Everybody got a bowl of soup and a slice of bread whether they accomplished what they were supposed to or not. It was the evening meal that was fed only to those who fulfilled their norm.

Activity sped up considerably during the afternoon hours. Even the Russian "stachanoviets" worked more diligently. They were now putting an expanse of roofing over one of the sections. The structure was very simple. The rear wall of the building was two logs higher than the front wall, so the roofing boards slanted at a certain degree to the front. They were then covered by a layer of tar paper and another layer of asbestos-like square sheets overlapping one another. Once the roof was on, the rest of the work could be done inside, out of the weather and everybody was looking forward to that. Room partitions, windows, doors and the stone and brick "piechka" were still to be done before the rooms would be ready for new occupants. Finally the dinner tokens were passed out to the workers, and they collected their evening meal, consisting again of a portion of kasha with oil and a slice of bread. Wozniak stopped in later that evening quite agitated.

"Dr. Helman was called in by the commandant an hour ago. I am really worried about him," he told Vita. "What do you suppose they wanted him for?"

"Leave the door open," suggested Vita. "We might hear him walking by."

"Oh, by the way, thank you for the pin. I had a talk with one of the "stachanoviets" yesterday. He lives in a village not too far from here and goes home one day each week. I thought he might be willing to barter with me. His wife works at a textile mill. He was telling me how well they were doing. She probably steals anything she can carry home. You know, they call it here 'na levo' — living on the left — bribing, bartering, exchanging goods for favors. Not quite criminal, but also not quite kosher."

And then they heard the footsteps. Wozniak leaned out the door and motioned to the doctor to come in. Dr. Helman slipped in and closed the door behind him.

"What did he want? Is everything all right?"

"Yes, yes. It had nothing to do with us. Did you know he has his whole family here?"

"No. We have seen him only once at that meeting."

"Well, anyway," Helman continued, "his little boy has a sore throat and is running a fever. I am apparently the only physician here, so he called me. I told him what it was and that I needed a supply of drugs to treat him as I had nothing to work with. His wife was very worried. Apparently the boy has been ill for a few days and isn't getting any better. I told him if the fever continued, they should take him to a hospital. The nearest hospital is in Beresnik, which is quite a distance from here. I said I would be glad to take the boy there, but he replied that would not be necessary. He would take him himself."

"Damn!" said Wozniak. "That would have been a great opportunity for you to get some information, pick up a newspaper and maybe some drugs."

"I know, but I did not want to push him. He was very business-like, but his wife was sympathetic. I could see it in her face. I told her about Sarah, and it made quite an impression on her. What do you suppose they are doing here? A high-ranking officer of the Soviet Army, with a family, running a labor camp?"

"I am sure it's a punishment for some transgression," said Wozniak. "Our Mr. Stalin and his NKVD don't tolerate even the slightest insubordination."

"Didn't you say the same thing about the major commanding our train?" asked Vita.

"Yes, exactly."

"Well, I better get back to my room. The children will be worried."

Vita latched the door after them and, taking the little lamp to the table, wrote down that day's news. She sat there for the longest time thinking about Helman's comments about the commandant's wife.

"Mother, you better get some sleep. We've got to be up at six tomorrow."

Several days went by with no news from Wozniak. Vita would see him at the construction site, and all he would do was shake his head: "No, not yet."

The building progressed rapidly and new rooms were finished, one by one. Metal smoke chimneys were installed in the stoves and stuck through large holes in the walls, left open for that purpose. A metal flange clamped to the pipe, filled the square opening in the wall, and scraps of the asbestos roof sheets were nailed to the logs all around the flange.

The Russian workers must have put up thousands of these buildings, all the same size, all with the same equipment. It became such a routine, there was never a moment's hesitation. Slap, bang, and a room was ready! Anya, Ellie and several other young women were assigned to plaster the inside seams between the logs with a white cement-like mixture. They became quite proficient at it, squeezing the goop between the logs and smoothing it with wooden trowels.

"Is that your boy out there?" one Russian worker asked Vita, pointing to Ellie. She almost corrected him, but thought better of it.

"Yes, why?"

"He is a good little worker. How old is he?"

"Just fifteen."

She repeated that conversation to Ellie that night, expecting a reaction, but all the girl said was, "Oh, I don't care. As a matter of fact, I am glad. You should see the looks and remarks Anya has to put up with!"

There was a knock on the door and Ellie let Wozniak in. He was obviously excited.

"I made contact today. My man is willing to barter! I showed him the pin and his eyes lit up. It is very nice, by the way. You sure you want to part with it?"

"Yes, yes! What can we get for it?"

"I don't know yet. He is going home tonight. We will know tomorrow. And that's not all. Bernie Helman went back to the commandant's. The boy is better. He told them that his tonsils might have to come out. He had a long talk with both of them. We are apparently to be moved into the new section. These quarters are just temporary. Normally these are assigned to the Russian workers. They are closer to the kitchen and the center of the camp."

"That would be quite an improvement. Everything is new and clean," said Vita.

"And another bonus!" Wozniak took out a small pouch of tobacco and a piece of neatly folded newspaper.

"I don't know whether I can stand all this in one evening!" Vita accepted the cigarette and a light and inhaled the smoke with relish. Wozniak divided the tobacco and paper.

"There will be more tomorrow!"

She had barely closed her eyes when a commotion and voices in the hallway made them all sit up in their cots. Ellie cracked the door open and saw Dr. Helman and Stan Kucharski in front of the Kos's room.

"Mr. Kos had a stroke, Ellie. Tell your mother," said the doctor.

"Is he all right?"

"No, I am afraid not."

They walked over to the Kos's room. The body was covered with a blanket and Mrs. Kos sat on a bench, her face in her hands, crying quietly. Vita walked over and gently touched the woman's shoulder.

"He is at peace now."

The woman looked up, nodding her head.

"He was always so upset and angry. It finally killed him. They are responsible, they did it! What will they do with him now?"

"I am sure we will find out tomorrow morning. I will stay with you for a while."

She sat next to the old woman, not knowing what to do or what to say.

Funerals were non-existent at Camp Vozemka. As soon as the officials were informed of the death, a committee quickly took over. Kos was placed in a wooden box; the widow was told that he would be transported in the afternoon on a truck into the village and buried there. She was not allowed to go along. Tearfully, she protested. It was cruel and barbaric to treat people like this.

"You are responsible! You killed him!" she told the head of the committee.

"Babushka," he answered, "he was an old man. He would have died anyway, anywhere."

Life meant nothing to them. It was a dispensable commodity they had plenty of.

****

Work proceeded as usual. That seemed to be the magical, all important word: "ROBOTA" — work — not just there in the camp, but throughout the entire Soviet Union. To get as much of an effort out of each individual body regardless of cost had become the way of life. All for the common good. There was never any personal profit, just meager rations of food and a scale payment in rubles. But the incredible thing about that was the fact that there was nothing to buy with the earned money throughout the entire country. The stores were empty and, if occasionally some supplies were delivered, people stood in long lines for hours to buy half a pound of sugar, salt or flour. Inevitably, in a short time, the store doors closed and the remaining long line was told, "All gone! There will be more tomorrow." But tomorrow would sometimes come a month or two later, perhaps never. There were few complainers, and those who did, were sent to Siberia. It was that simple.

The camp "store" had had no shipment of any kind of provisions since January. They could, however, buy as many boxes of tooth powder as they wanted. The shelves were filled with them. A full-time sales clerk was always on duty promising "good tomorrows." It became a joke among Vita's group. Any question relating to food or other necessity was always answered with: "Zahvtrah, zahvtrah (tomorrow)!" No wonder theft and bartering flourished in the USSR.

Saturday was, for some odd reason, the day designated as a rest day. The prisoners could sleep longer, do some cleaning and washing, go to the bathhouse, split wood for the "piechka," mend torn clothing, and generally take care of other necessities there was no time for during working days.

The word got around that there was a doctor in the camp now, and Helman was constantly called to patch up an axe wound, lance a boil, or simply give advice when there was nothing he could do. Without proper instruments, or even an aspirin to give out, he was totally helpless. He would come back from these "rounds" dejected and disgusted.

"You should see how these people live. You have no idea how grateful I am to be part of your group," he would tell them. "Nobody lifts a finger over there. They are all Orthodox Jews, mostly merchants, rabbis, peddlers. None of them has ever held an axe or a saw in his hands. They have no idea how to use them; and when they do, they hack themselves to pieces! I have got to go back to patch up a leg that's bleeding very badly. Mrs. Kew, can you come with me to hold the light?"

"I would love to help you," replied Vita, "but I can't stand the sight of blood!"

"I'll go," volunteered Ellie.

Dr. Helman was rolling up strips of an old sheet he had previously boiled to use as bandages. He placed them on a clean towel adding another small bundle containing a paring knife, well-sharpened by Mr. Kos, and a pair of small scissors. He used one of his cooking pots as a "sterilizer."

"All right, Ellie. Are you sure you can handle it?" he asked, handing her the lantern.

"Positive!"

"Now, Ellie, don't touch anything or anybody out there, understand?" admonished Vita as they left the building.

The stench hit them as soon as they opened the hall door. Helman handed Ellie a folded piece of cloth and told her to put it over her mouth and nose and breathe through it. He led the way down the dirty hallway to the fourth door and went in with Ellie right behind him. This room was relatively clean and had only two occupants in it: a man lying on a cot and a woman boiling something on the stove.

"Come in, doctor," she said. "I sent a friend out to borrow some towels. Ours are all bloody."

Dr. Helman uncovered the man's leg exposing an ugly gash across his shin bone. The blood was still oozing out of the wound. He tied a narrow belt above the man's knee and started to clean the leg up the best he could. He then wrapped the shin tightly with his makeshift clean bandage, pressing the wound together. Ellie held up the light.

"This should be stitched up, but I have nothing to do it with. Here is another bandage. If the blood soaks through, wrap it again real tight. I will stop in in a couple of days."

He removed the belt from the man's leg and put it in his pocket.

"Thank you, doctor," the man said. "It was stupid of me to do this, but the axe bounced off a tree, and it's so heavy and sharp, it just...."

"I know, I know. You have probably never used an axe before, have you?"

"Well, not really."

"How long have you two been here?" asked Helman.

"Six days."

"Well, good luck. I have to go now. The most important thing is to keep the wound clean. I have nothing to give you, not even an aspirin. It will probably hurt like hell for a few days because you chipped some of the bone, but I can't help you."

He shook the young man's hand and, collecting his tools, led Ellie out into the stinking hallway.

"We were lucky. These were clean people; you should see some of the other rooms!"

"I don't have to, I can smell them," the girl answered, pressing the cloth to her nose. Once outside, they took deep breaths of fresh air and hurried to their barracks.

"I enjoyed doing this, Dr. Helman. If you need me again, I will be glad to help."

"Thank you, Nurse Ellie. I will certainly remember that."

****

14

NO WORK - NO FOOD!

June 14th, 1940.
The German Army marched into Paris,
and on June 22nd France signed an armistice with Germany.
August 1940 the Battle of Britain began.
September 3rd, London endured the Blitzkrieg!

The weather was changing rapidly. The snow had all melted and it was warm enough to shed heavy clothing. Spring in Siberia? Was that possible?

Because more Russians were being shipped up and located in the center buildings, Vita's group was moved into the new barracks. They were delighted with the fresh, clean rooms, one to each family, seven in all, in one long row, close together. Vita and Ellie had a room to themselves, as the two little girls were moved to stay with Mrs. Kos, the official babysitter. The smell of new, raw wood was so strong, they had to keep their doors and the hallway doors open to air it out. Some new prisoners were moved into the rest of the building, and Helman was elected to keep an eye on them and make sure they kept their quarters clean.

Wozniak's man was a great source of contraband, trading his goods for Vita's trinkets. Each week he brought back a few items and the two of them would decide how to put them to best use. Food was usually shared with the others. Tobacco went to the smokers. Clothing items and pieces of fabric were divided among the women for scarves, hats, mittens or anything that Vita could cut and sew up, mostly for the children. Nella and Dorotka now had spare, clean clothes.

Food was the most cherished barter item. One day they got ten fresh eggs! After a long conference, they decided that each child should get an egg. There were ten children in the group.

Vita held her daughter's egg, wondering what to do with it.

"Ellie, how would you like it?"

"Soft boiled," Ellie decided. "No, hard boiled — that way we can share it."

"Oh, no, this one is all yours," said Vita. "When we get some more, I shall have one."

"When we do get them, we will share them again. Please, Mother, I will not eat the whole egg, and that is final!"

Vita plopped the egg into water and they both watched it boil. Ellie toasted a slice of bread; and when the egg was ready, she peeled it and cut it in half. It was the best thing they had eaten in a long time. This is pathetic, thought Vita, watching Ellie relish every little bite.

The extra housing now complete, the building crew was transferred to work as lumberjacks in the vast ancient forests. Lumber in all forms was the only product exported out of that region. At one of the meetings, the chief supervisor of all the working crews outlined the kind of work that would be expected from the internees.

"Trees will be cut down and marked as to their best use," the chief was saying. "Did you know that our lumber is sought after by the largest ship builders in the entire world? We have the best, tallest, straightest trees here. We are very proud of the products we ship out of this camp, and we expect you to do first class work."

The group exchanged sidelong glances. Vita kept her eyes on the commandant, Igor Ivanovich, who sat at the head table, twirling and untwirling a piece of paper. He looked completely disinterested in what the supervisor was saying. Occasionally, he scanned the rows of the prisoners, moving his head imperceptibly from side to side. He looked over Vita's group carefully, taking his time, observing each person. He stared at Vita. She glared back, never blinking, never averting her eyes, her teeth clenched, her jaw jutting out.

"Mother," hissed Ellie, tugging at her sleeve. "What are you doing?"

"Nothing, sweetheart, I am letting him know I am not afraid of him," she whispered back.

The meeting was now coming to an end with the usual singing routine. They were learning another patriotic song about the Red Army and some field on which the soldiers rode to victory! It was utter nonsense!

****

The dense, beautiful forest encircled the campsite. Groups of approximately fifty internees were led by two guards to the different work sites. The eleven working adults in Vita's group kept together and were assigned to the same area. Mrs. Kos stayed behind, taking care of the six small children and Sarah Helman, who wandered aimlessly, oblivious to everything around her.

Vita dabbed her lips with a small stub of lipstick she had saved for special occasions.

"Well, Ellie, let's go!" she said, hoisting an axe over her shoulder.

"Here, Mother, let me carry that for you."

"Oh, no, I want to do it myself. I wish one of us had a camera. Wouldn't it make a wonderful souvenir?"

They had to walk quite a distance to their assigned area. Work was already in progress breaking the silence of the woods with loud chopping and sawing noises and the whoosh and clatter of falling trees.

"Hey, you there! Get out of the way!" someone shouted. A loud crash followed the warning as another huge tree hit the ground.

"Holy Jesus!" exclaimed Stan Kucharski. "It's a real massacre! Look at these beautiful trees. At this rate there will be no more forests left!"

The group was quickly divided — the men to cut and saw and fell trees, some of the women to strip branches and bark and drag them to the bonfire. Vita and Ellie were ordered to cut the tree trunks into meter-long segments and stack them between posts into cubic-meter piles. They were given a long, two-man saw with large, sharp teeth and a handle at each end. Vita couldn't imagine being able to man the long saw effectively.

"Tovarish," she called to the guard. "You can't possibly expect us to do this kind of work. I can't even move the log!"

He quickly showed her how. By using a long pole, shaped into a wedge at the end, and prying it under the fallen tree, lifting it slightly, he rolled the log along the ground with ease. Ellie got the idea immediately.

"Leverage, Mother, here let me do it."

She lifted the thinner end of a tree trunk with the pole and rolled it over onto a smaller branch, placed perpendicular to the log.

"See, now it's off the ground and we can cut it."

"Remember, five cubic feet per worker!" repeated the guard.

"They are all mad. We can't do this. I simply refuse to!" Vita sat down on one of the logs, looking around desperately. Helman walked over and crouched beside her.

"They can't make me!" she kept saying.

"Oh, yes, they can. They will simply not feed you; and if you persist, they will jail you. That's the system. You just have to go along; we'll all help. Come on, give Ellie a hand; she is trying very hard."

****

There was never enough space in her little calendar to write all her thoughts, feelings and describe the events, in spite of all the abbreviations she used. And on top of it, Ellie fought her all along.

"Mother, please throw that book away. Do you realize what would happen if they found it? I am sure we will remember all this when we get out."

"No, Ellie. I have got to do this. This is documentation, dates and places, it's all there. If anything happens to me, I want you to see to it that your father gets it. He will know what to do. This sort of thing should never be forgotten!"

****

No matter how hard they tried, they could never fulfill the quota. They were always two or three cubic meters short of their required ten. Without their food tokens, they went to bed hungry. Ellie never complained for fear of what her mother would do.

One afternoon, taking her cigarette break, Vita kept looking at the red crayon marks their guard made the previous night on one of the logs in each completed stack.

"How many have we got today?" she asked.

"Seven."

"See the four last stacks we cut yesterday? All right, here's what we will do. Where are the guards now?"

"By the fire. Mother, what are you up to?"

"Go behind each of the stacks and try to push the middle log out a little. No, not that one, the one with the mark on it! Pound it a little with a piece of wood if you can't push. Don't worry about the guards; I am watching them. Hand me the small saw. Now, you go over to the fire and ask the guards what time it is or anything you can think of — it's all right, you are on your break."

"Mother, what...."

"Just go!" There was that look again. Those eyes drilled right through her. Ellie walked over to the bonfire and engaged one of the guards in a short conversation. When she came back, her mother was stacking the last cubic meter they had just cut.

"Here, give me a hand with the heavy one."

Then she held up a thin, measuring stick to the new pile, cocking her head to one side and squinting at it.

"Yes, that's perfect! We have got another one. Now we have more than our ten for today!"

"Mother, you are not going to get away with it," said Ellie scared half to death.

"I don't have the slightest idea what you are talking about."

The guards were now checking the completed work.

"We have eleven today!" exclaimed Vita, pointing to a row of neatly stacked logs.

"That is very good," he replied, marking the logs with his crayon. "Here are your two dinner tokens and one more for a job well done! Keep it up."

"I certainly will!" said Vita, giving him a bright smile.

When he was gone, Ellie wanted to know what her mother did with the marked up disks she sawed off the four logs.

"They are right here, under my sweater, and they are killing me. We will burn them when we get back. I wish you were a little braver, Ellie. It's our survival we are fighting for. It's either that or starvation. Tonight, with the extra portion of kasha, the tiny strip of bacon we still have from our last "deal" with Mr. Wozniak, and one potato, I will cook a pot of soup that will give us a couple of meals. I am sure you noticed how thin we are both getting. Dr. Helman is afraid that if we don't get some fresh vegetables and meat, we will all suffer from malnutrition, especially the children. This is very serious."

"I know, Mother, but what happens when we get caught?"

"Well, we will worry about that if and when it happens! In the meantime, mum's the word. I don't want you telling anybody about our secret, particularly Anya. She is getting very chummy with one of the guards. Her mother is quite upset."

"He is not the only one she is chummy with," said Ellie knowingly. But that was all she would say, and Vita knew better than to pry.

****

Late at night, with the lamp turned down low, Vita filled the little pages of her calendar. May was almost over; the days were long, sunny and warm and she marveled at the fact that this cursed land could be so beautiful. The woods were alive with a variety of wild flowers under the huge majestic trees. Clumps of white birches, now all leafed out and interspersed by tall dark-green pines, looked as if some giant landscaper had arranged them, carefully picking and assembling his favorite shades of colors and varieties of vegetation.

Wild strawberries bloomed profusely, promising a big crop of berries. Vita could hardly wait — fresh fruit! There were other varieties of berry bushes all around the labor camp. This could be their salvation. She worried about her bleeding gums and canker sores. The ugly word "trench mouth" kept nagging at her. She remembered hearing about it as a child. World War I soldiers suffered from it due to lack of adequate diet.

She also noticed with alarm the many sores and infected scratches, mostly on the children's legs and arms. They were just ordinary mosquito bites and under normal conditions would have been ignored, but here they developed into ugly, festering boils with black tissue growing wide and deep. These were hard to heal. They had to be scraped clean and kept covered. Dr. Helman wondered if this was not Pellagra, a disease brought on by niacin deficiency. The new crop of mosquitoes, rising from the marshy lands, was large and their bites were vicious.

"Scrub your arms and legs with the grey lye soap and above all don't scratch!" admonished the doctor, but that was easier said than done.

In one of Wozniak's bartering deals, he received a bottle of vodka. After much haranguing among the group as to its best use, it was turned over to Helman for medicinal purposes.

"Look, this is one hundred percent proof spirit. I can use it as a disinfectant. I have nothing else right now. If we drink it, it will be wasted," he argued.

"Oh, hell, here I thought we would have a party!" Stan Kucharski chuckled.

****

Dr. Helman was again summoned to the commandant's office.

"There will be a large shipment of medicine coming in," he announced. "I want you to help with the distribution."

"Thank you very much. What are we getting?"

"Quinine and atabrine."

"Quinine? But Igor Ivanovich, that's used to treat malaria. Malaria is a tropical disease. In this climate...."

"Yes, we do have outbreaks of malaria," the commandant interrupted, "and that's what we are getting. Make the best use you can of it."

Helman was dismissed and walked back to the barracks shaking his head. What a system, he thought. That night he told the group about it.

"Can you imagine feeding quinine indiscriminately to just anybody?"

"Has it got any other use?" asked Vita.

"Oh, certainly! It stimulates appetite."

They all looked at each other and burst out laughing.

****

Life went on. Incredible as it seemed, the human body's resilience seemed unlimited. Vita kept up her diary on a nightly basis. In spite of the minimal nutrition, hard work and practically no medical attention, her mind was as alert as ever — always scheming, always inventing some new ways to improve their lot, even by the smallest degree.

She marveled at the strength her arms and her calloused hands developed. She was constantly on the alert to invent new ways to achieve their quota of work. The young guard assigned to her group paid more attention to Anya Karowska than to his work, and Ellie was Anya's friend. He was all smiles, checking off their completed stacks of wood, sometimes two or three cubic meters over the required norm! He called them "stachanoviets" — superior workers, and offered extra food tokens. Vita also noticed that Mrs. Karowska and her daughter Anya somehow filled their required quota on a daily basis and received their food rations. The young man was very generous!

At one of the weekly meetings, the "stachanoviets" of that group were "honored." Their names were read and, as they stood, the chief supervisor told them that they would be the first to receive winter clothing when it was shipped to the camp.

Vita kept up her routine of glaring at the commandant. She never took her eyes off him. It was a belligerent, challenging stare. It said: You dirty "sukin syn"! She was determined to force his attention. She wanted to see him, to talk to him. With the exception of Dr. Helman, nobody was allowed to go near his quarters. Several of his aides dealt with the camp's problems, and his office was off limits to the prisoners. There had to be a way. She was determined to find it.

****

A commotion and loud screams for help made them all drop their tools and run over to a new work area where a large crew had started to cut down some of the biggest trees. One of them had fallen slightly off its mark and crushed several workers.

Dozens of men and women tried frantically to get to them through the mass of huge branches, heavy with wet leaves.

"Get the doctor! Hurry!"

Helman was already there, pushing through the crowd gathered around, watching helplessly.

"We've got to get them out! I can't even see where they are!" shouted Helman.

Some of the men ran for their saws and started cutting away branch after branch.

"Oh, God, there are four of them," sobbed one of the women.

The doctor was kneeling down beside the crushed men, clearing off bunches of wet leaves, looking for signs of life, feeling their pulses.

"Get the guards over here!" demanded Helman.

Four of them came running, shoving away the stunned workers crowding around the fallen tree.

"What's going on here?"

"Two are dead," reported Helman. "The other two are still alive. I need help. Get me some blankets or something to carry them on, and I want permission from the commandant to take them to the hospital. Has the truck left?"

"No, not yet," someone said.

Two of the guards hurried to the campsite. Somebody produced a couple of blankets and a table top, and under Helman's supervision the two badly injured men were lifted onto the improvised stretcher and carried to a clearing. One of them was moaning, trying to move his arms. Helman bent over him.

"Try to keep still. You will be fine. We will get you to a hospital."

There was no sound or movement out of the other injured.

The chief labor supervisor was now on the scene, questioning the witnesses.

"We really don't know what went wrong here," answered one of the Russian laborers. "It was a very tall and big tree, and with all the rain we had last night, the crown must have been much heavier on one side than the other and it just twisted and fell the wrong way. It could have been much worse."

The chief supervisor hurried to report to the commandant. After a few minutes, Helman was called into the office.

"How bad are they?" Igor Ivanovich wanted to know.

"Very bad. You have got to let me take them in to Beresnik. I can't do anything for them here!"

"All right," he snapped. "Vanya, you go with him." The young soldier acknowledged the order and rushed out to instruct the truck driver.

"Comrade, can you please give me some written request to get a few necessary drugs and instruments. I am helpless out here! Remember your son? We could have gotten him well much faster had I had some sulfa or aspirin...."

The commandant's wife was now standing in the doorway.

"Iggy, please, the doctor is right."

"Okay, okay." He yanked a sheet of paper out of his desk and wrote a few sentences. Helman thanked them, folding the paper and putting it in his pocket.

The two injured men were already in the truck bed, and the driver was stoking the fires under the water tanks. What a way to propel an engine, thought Helman, climbing onto the tailgate and crouching next to the two injured men.

"You really don't need this," he said to the young soldier, pointing to his rifle. "I am not running away."

"I have my orders," replied Vanya, shrugging his shoulders.

"How far is it?"

"Well, it's ten kilometers to the village, and then another fifteen or twenty to Beresnik. We can probably use the regular road if it's not under water."

The trip took almost an hour, but finally they approached the entrance to the

Beresnik General Hospital. Vanya marched inside and soon came out with two attendants and a hospital cart.

"We need two," demanded Helman.

"Who is he?" one of the attendants asked Vanya.

"A doctor from the camp."

"They let him out?"

"Please," Helman interrupted the conversation. "This is an emergency. These men are dying!"

"Da, da, we know, we get them all the time," remarked one of the attendants, moving the cart close to the truck gate.

They moved the unconscious man first. Bright red, foamy blood was oozing out of the corners of his mouth.

"He doesn't look too good, does he?" observed Vanya.

They rolled the cart into the hospital entrance. It took forever, it seemed, for them to come back to collect the second man. Helman's patience was wearing out, but he kept calm outwardly. He wanted to meet the doctor. He hoped to gain his sympathy and understanding for the predicament he was in. He wanted supplies, medicines, and most of all information. This was his first contact with the outside world; he had to be very careful how he handled it.

"Are you a relative?" he heard someone ask.

"No, I brought them here. I am a doctor from Camp Vozemka. How are they?"

"One of them is gone — internal bleeding. The other might have a chance. Multiple fractures and injuries. We will see what we can do. What is going on in these camps? We get these types of injuries almost on a daily basis," he said in a low voice, making sure nobody overheard him.

"We are not used to hard labor. You can't imagine how many injuries I see at the camp that are not brought here. And I have nothing to work with! I was hoping you might be able to help me." He handed him the commandant's note.

"Well, we are just a small outpost hospital here, and our supplies are quite limited, but I will see what I can do. Go down to the kitchen and have some tea and a bite to eat. I will be right back."

"Dr....?" Helman didn't know his name.

"Prokopiev," he introduced himself.

His guard, Vanya, kept urging him to hurry. It was getting to be quite late, and he was anxious to get back to the camp.

"Go down to the dining room and get some good tea and sweet bread. Tell them Dr. Prokopiev sent you," suggested Helman. "I'll wait here for the final report."

Vanya's eyes lit up. "Good idea! I will be right back."

Dr. Prokopiev finally appeared and the two men stood in the ward's doorway.

"Here are a few things I could gather." He handed Helman two bundles of instruments wrapped in sterile towels, a bottle of sulfa powder, another of aspirin and iodine.

"You look disappointed," he said, observing Helman's fallen face. This is all I can do for you now."

"I know, and I am very grateful."

Back on the truck Vanya wanted to know what was in the package Helman was holding.

"It's something Dr. Prokopiev is sending the commandant, satisfied?"

They rode the rest of the way in silence.

That night the adults gathered in Vita's room, anxiously waiting for Dr. Helman's news from the outside world. To their disappointment, all he could tell them was the fact that one of the injured men survived and that he brought back with him a small supply of medicines and a few instruments. Jan Wozniak was visibly upset with him.

"Didn't you talk with anybody? Couldn't you get a newspaper? Can't you tell us anything? That was an opportunity we may never get again!"

"Look, I did the best I could. Vanya was watching me constantly, and I did get a few things. I admit it isn't much, but I am sure that the commandant now trusts me and will send me out again."

Wozniak just waved his arm and, mouthing something inaudible, walked out.

"He is just frustrated," said Vita. "What is the hospital like?"

"It's rather a primitive setup, more like an army field hospital than a regular one, but they do have several wards and operating facilities and I met a very nice, decent doctor who runs the place. He gave me two small kits with just the basic few instruments — a scalpel, surgical scissors, a probe and a couple of clamps. Again, those look like army issue and are of poor quality, but they are better than nothing! We also have some iodine and sulfa powder. Oh, and a small supply of aspirin. I just don't understand why Wozniak is so upset with me."

"You know him. He was so excited all day long, couldn't wait for you to get back. I can't imagine what he expected to hear from you, but I wouldn't worry about it. He will calm down," said Vita.

After the men left, Vita and Greta Karowska were finishing their cigarettes. They devised a method by which they could smoke the little stub to the bitter end without burning their fingers. A hair pin made a perfect handle.

"I am so worried about Anya," Mrs. Karowska finally said. "She is going through a difficult and awkward period. She won't talk to me; she won't listen. I know she is seeing one of the guards; you know which one, Ellie, don't you?"

"I don't know anything about it, Mrs. Karowska," replied Ellie, stretching out on her cot.

"But you are her friend; you are always with her; she spends most of her evenings with you."

Vita and Ellie exchanged glances.

"And how about you, Ellie dear; don't the guards bother you?"

"Mrs. Karowska, most of the Russians think I am a boy, and I don't have any problems."

"Well, I suppose Anya is just too pretty for her own good."

She bid them good night and left, weighted down by concern and worry.

"Ellie," said her mother. "Can you tell me what is going on? Anya says she is spending the evenings with you. She is obviously not coming here. So where is she going?"

"I don't know, Mother!" She turned to face the wall and closed her eyes.

Ellie accompanied Bernie Helman on his nightly rounds as a matter of routine now. The commandant provided the doctor with a small room in one of the barracks, and he set up "office hours" after the evening meal for those who could navigate on their own. But there were many sick and injured who could not walk anymore, and those were visited after the office hours.

The days were now so long that the sun set in the middle of the night and came up again very early in the morning. Outside there was no need for a lantern, but some of the rooms were dark, their windows draped with rags. These barracks were set up for single men only, so the rooms were much larger and housed several men. Those were the worst.

"Here, Ellie, give me the light. You stay outside. This is pretty bad; there are two old men in there who won't last much longer."

"What's wrong with them?"

"Starvation, dehydration — same old thing. You know what they say — no work, no food. These people either could not work anymore or simply refused to go, so they were not fed. Very simple and, as you know, you can only survive so long."

"Why are they that way? Can't they try like we do? Can't they at least try to work and keep themselves clean? I don't understand this. You are Jewish, Dr. Helman, and you are not that way."

"I am not an Orthodox Jew. A lot of those people are fatalists; they can't help it."

"What does that mean?"

"They believe very strongly that if fate deals them this sort of lot in life, they can't or won't do anything about it; they just accept it. It is very sad, but true. And don't forget these are very poor people who were raised in ghettos. They never had any hope."

"Can't you tell them that this will not last forever? My mother is sure we will get out of here, and so am I, sometimes."

He looked down at her troubled face.

"Nurse, we have work to do." She smiled at him. He was a dear, good man, and she liked him a lot.

****

Summer, 1940. The wild strawberries were ripening in such profusion throughout the woods that Ellie and Vita could gather a small bucketful during their lunch time and still have enough time to consume their portion of soup brought to them at noon. The strawberries were unusually large for the wild variety, very sweet and delicious.

"Don't overdo it," warned Helman. "You are not used to fresh fruit. Eat a little at a time. I don't want any complaints about bellyaches!"

But he couldn't stop the children from gobbling up handfuls of the berries while gathering them. The temptation was too great. The predicted results were immediately evidenced by frequent, mad dashes for the latrines.

"Ellie, did you have to go again? How many times?" asked Vita.

"Many, Mother, but it was worth it!" Ellie grinned back at her.

I wonder if we could cook them, Vita was thinking, make some sort of sauce or compote. That night she tried it, but it made their room unbearably hot.

"We will have to do this outside, Ellie. Can you build us a little stone fire pit to set this pot on?"

"Oh, sure, I can do that very easily. Mother, do you suppose if we cook the berries very long, we can make jam?"

"That's a very good idea! We have no sugar, but we can certainly try to cook it down until it thickens enough to spread on bread."

"When was the last shipment of sugar?" asked Ellie.

"Two months ago."

"You know, if we ever get out of here and I have enough white bread and sugar, I will never ask for anything else."

WE ARE GOING TO SURVIVE! she wrote down that night in her diary. And then she repeated it and underlined it. And that was all she entered under that date.

****

Wozniak lost his bartering man. He evidently served out his detention and went home; but Jan was romancing someone else. His younger daughter was a sickly child, and he desperately needed to supplement her diet with other nutrients beside kasha and black bread. Milk was not available to the prisoners. The commandant received a container of it for his children. It was brought up on the truck from the neighboring kolhoz once a week. There had to be some way he could get his hands on at least a small portion for his child.

****

Dr. Helman made several trips to Beresnik, hauling the injured and the very sick, but he was always under guard, unable to make contact with any outsiders except Dr. Prokopiev and the hospital staff. People were dying at an alarming rate of all sorts of causes. Malnutrition and accidents were the underlying factors except for an outbreak of typhoid fever, which also claimed a number of the old and weak.

"Boil all the water and wash your hands before you touch any food," ordered Helman, frantically running from barrack to barrack to assess the number of the sick and report it to the commandant.

"Is it very contagious?" Igor Ivanovich wanted to know.

"Well, it is spread through contaminated water and food. The germs are not airborne if that's what you mean. I don't know where this is coming from, so please boil everything...water, milk, and keep your hands as clean as possible. I am afraid we will lose a lot of people."

"Well, my friend, you and I are doing the best we can, aren't we?" said Igor Ivanovich, patting Helman on his back.

****

Stan Kucharski came running back to the barracks all excited.

"Hey, ladies, they are unloading a shipment of goods at the store. You better go. There is a line there already."

"Do you know what it is?"

"No, but the boxes are quite large!"

Vita dropped the laundry she was hanging out and corralled one of the smaller children, "Go find Ellie, will you please. She is in the woods picking berries."

She then made a mad dash for the store to stand in the line, which was already quite long. Mrs. Karowska and Marta Kucharska were right behind her.

"I heard there is flour and sugar today!" someone ahead of them was saying.

It took about an hour for the salesclerk to get everything ready and then another hour for Vita's turn. The rations were allotted per person this time, so she was relieved to see Ellie and the others further down in line. They each collected half a pound of flour, a chunk of sugar approximately 100 grams, two meters of cotton calico material and a bar of soap.

"What's in those boxes down there?" Vita wanted to know.

"Those are not for you," replied the clerk.

"Oh, really? Who are they for?" Mrs. Karowska chimed in.

"None of your business. Move along!" The clerk was getting irritated.

They gathered their items and walked out of the store.

"What was in those tins, could you tell?"

"It looked like soup in some of them and ham or some other kind of meat in the smaller tins. I bet those go to the Russian stachanoviets."

"Well," Vita said, "aren't we stachanoviets too?"

"I wonder what it would take to get a job as the clerk's helper?" said Marta Kucharska. "We would have all the meat we wanted."

"You mean...." Mrs. Karowska made a sweeping gesture with her hand landing in her pocket.

"Sure. They all do it. Stan made friends with some of the Russian workers, and they bragged about how much stuff they pilfered from the kolhoses or factories they worked in. Apparently, it's a way of life under this system."

They shook their heads in dismay.

Vita looked over their newly acquired provisions. She would make two sheets and two pillow cases for their cots out of the fabric. It was very wide, so she was sure there would be a lot left over for other things. The sugar she would chip into tiny chunks for their "tea," which actually was hot water. Tea was non-existent. Because there was never enough sugar to sweeten a whole cup of water, they learned from the Russians to drink it "na prikusku." You placed a tiny sliver of the hard, solid sugar under your tongue and sipped the hot water, hoping for it to last. Ellie had her own method. She would drink half of the cup without sugar and then have enough to sweeten the rest.

****

Dr. Helman examined the funny spots on Ellie's face and neck and announced that she had chicken pox! There were several other cases around the camp, he told them.

"I knew you would pick up something dreadful on those damned rounds," fumed Vita. "You ought to know better than to drag this child through the filthy barracks," she turned on Helman.

"She didn't necessarily pick it up out there. Dorotka just came down with it this morning, and my two children have it too." Helman tried to calm her down. "They seem to be all light cases; just don't scratch the spots! We don't want any pock marks on your face."

Ellie's pox lasted quite a bit longer than the smaller children's, and Helman made sure she was excused from work and given her full food rations. It was wonderful to be able to sleep late in the mornings and sit out in the sun during the day, watching the simmering strawberry jam, so it wouldn't burn, or just do nothing at all. Do nothing and think back. Remember that other life. Imagine, just a year ago, school was over and.... Tears filled her eyes. It's all my fault. I should have listened; I should have understood what was going on! How stupid and selfish of me....

"Ellie, you all right? Why are you crying?" Anya was kneeling beside her.

"God, you startled me! What are you doing here in the middle of the day? You got the pox too?"

"No, it's the strawberries, I think. They really upset my stomach. I have been barfing for days now. They let me take the rest of the day off."

"We are cooking ours. Mother thinks this sauce, or jam, or whatever it is, will not give us the runs."

"Oh, really? Let me try some."

Ellie dipped out a spoonful of the simmering thick sauce and handed it to Anya. She made a face, tasting it. "It's awfully sour and bitter, isn't it?"

"Why, certainly, silly, there is no sugar in it!"

Ellie took another, closer look at her friend.

"You look awful. You sure you don't have the pox?"

"Yah, I am sure. I don't have any fever or any spots like you do. Will those mark up your face permanently?"

"Dr. Helman says that if I don't scratch the scabs off, I won't have any marks. They itch so terribly, though, you want to rip them off!"

They spent the rest of the afternoon sitting around the small fire, stirring the jam and talking.

****

Resourcefulness was something Vita never seemed to lack.

"I'll give you fifty rubles if you save me some of those empty jars the beets come in," she whispered to the cook, collecting her extra portion of kasha.

"That's nice. Have you got a little something else?"

"Like what?"

"You got a watch?"

"Watch? For empty jars you are going to throw out? How about a nice string of pearls for your wife?"

"Okay, I will have the jars ready for you tomorrow."

The fake pearls will do just fine, she thought. Her plan was to boil the jars clean, fill them with the thick fruit marmalade and seal it with a thin layer of wax. She would melt the two candles she had been saving in case her lamp oil ran out. This should preserve the jam at least for a few months. She would do the same thing with the now ripening blueberries, wild raspberries and later on the most favorite of them all, the lingonberries.

****

The girls were in the woods gathering kindling. It was Saturday, their day off. It was warm and sunny. Anya put her bundle of sticks on the ground and motioned to Ellie to sit down for awhile.

"I am very tired. Let's rest a bit, shall we?"

Ellie looked at her friend carefully. "Don't you feel well? You look sick."

"Well, I think I am. I skipped last month. You know, the curse. I am terrified."

"Anya, I haven't had it for some time either!"

"You?"

"Sure, and Mother and some of the other ladies. Dr. Helman explained it to us. It has something to do with nature, some defense mechanism. When you are in a rundown condition, it stops by itself! Isn't it great?"

"Yah, for you maybe."

"What do you mean, for me?"

"I want you to swear to me you will not breathe a word to anybody... not a soul, understand?"

"Yes, sure, I swear." Ellie's heart skipped a beat. She could guess what she was about to hear.

"Well, I have been spending a lot of time with Jerzy. I really like him. He is..."

"Jerzy? I thought you were sneaking around with that guard of ours?"

"I have only done it with him twice, I swear, just to keep him on our side. How do you suppose we get all the food tokens?"

"Are you crazy? What is the matter with you?"

"Ellie, please, you are the only friend I have. You have got to help me!"

"Me? What do you expect me to do? Can't you talk to your mother or the doctor? It's probably nothing."

"Talk to my mother? I would just as soon hang myself." She was now dissolved in tears. "I am only 17, Ellie, what will happen to me?"

"I will do anything I can for you, just tell me what."

"Maybe you could find out from the doctor, just to make sure, maybe you are right maybe it's nothing... the nature stuff, like you said."

"Anya, I think you should talk to him yourself."

"No, no, no!"

"Listen, he is very nice and very good. He will never tell anybody if you don't want him to, I promise you. And, he is the only one who will know for sure. Maybe, you are worried for nothing."

"I hope to God you are right, Ellie."

Anya wiped her face and managed a smile. "I will think about it, and thank you very much."

That bit of news weighed heavily on Ellie's mind. She was preoccupied with it day and night, mulling it over and over. The most horrible thoughts kept nagging at her. She had just helped, in a very small way, with a delivery of a premature baby.

Dr. Helman was called, and she offered to carry his things and the lamp for him The mother, a young Russian girl, had syphilis Dr. Helman told her. The baby was born blind and completely covered with oozing blisters. It was horrible. It died the next day. When the doctor reported it to the commandant, he didn't seem very concerned.

"Yes, we do have quite a bit of that around the labor camps. One can't be too careful, can one?" And that was all. Helman was dismissed!

Ellie couldn't get that incident out of her mind. She kept asking the doctor about that particular disease. How did one get it? Was there a cure for it? Where did it come from?

"You are really interested in all this, aren't you?" he wondered.

"Well, yes. I might study medicine when we get back home."

"That's my girl," he said patting her shoulder. "I think you would make a very good doctor."

He was satisfied now and very gladly answered all the questions. He explained all the hypothetical situations she posed for him.

"Doctor, suppose you had a daughter who, you know, got herself in that sort of trouble out here in the camp with some Russian, what would you do to help her?"

"Ellie, are you trying to tell me something?"

"No, Dr. Helman, I am just curious," she smiled at him.

"Well, there are ways to terminate an unwanted pregnancy, but the reasons should be important enough to justify it. I would certainly consider it seriously with my hypothetical daughter. Satisfied?"

"Yes, thank you. I thought you would."

He was half-amused and half-concerned. What on earth brought all that on, he wondered.

****

Without a watch it was very difficult to distinguish the nights from the days. The sun almost never set. It was bright enough to read outside at midnight without any difficulty... a very confusing phenomenon. Wozniak explained that they were far north of the equator, and at certain times of the year the sun didn't set at all. It was June or July, he thought, but it wouldn't last very long. In the meantime, he suggested they cover the windows with dark cloths and use a blindfold over their eyes at night.

****

The chief supervisor came out of the office as the prisoners were gathering to be led off to work one morning.

"I need to reassign some of you to different work this morning," the chief was saying. He read about twenty names off his list. Vita and Ellie were among those. "We are short of fuel for our trucks. Follow Vanya, he will show you what to do."

They marched off wondering what now? The work proved to be much lighter and, by comparison, almost enjoyable! Piles and piles of already cut birch trees were waiting in a clearing. They were told to clean off the branches and cut the thin, long trunks into three inch chunks, then split the disks into four sections and throw them onto a mound to cure. This was fuel for the antiquated trucks that made their trips between the villages and the labor camps. Vanya, satisfied that the work was progressing well, went back to the camp.

"Mother, isn't this easy?" asked Ellie.

"I wonder how much we are supposed to produce per day?"

"Well, how can they measure this?"

Ellie would line up a row of the small disks on a large stump and chop them first in half and then into quarters. She would then throw the pieces onto a pile and urge the ladies to cut faster! After awhile she laid her axe down, examining her right forearm.

"Look, Mother, this really hurts," she said pointing to a swollen lump the size of a walnut.

"Oh dear, this looks terrible." The other women were also examining the swollen, inflamed lump halfway between her elbow and her wrist.

"Looks like a large boil," decided Mrs. Kucharska.

"I will show it to Dr. Helman tonight," said Ellie.

It was indeed a boil, Helman agreed, and advised Ellie to put hot, wet compresses on it to have it come to a head. Off work again, Ellie kept the outside burner going, heating water for her hot packs and nursing her arm. It was red and swollen and very painful. Helman examined it daily and finally decided that it would have to be lanced.

The arm was now swollen up to the elbow and Ellie couldn't use it at all.

"I am afraid this will hurt; I don't have anything to numb it with. I really hate to do it, but it doesn't look like it has a head and it is too large to just dissipate. We have got to open it up. See, the glands under your arm are enlarged. This is not going to get better by itself," Helman explained.

"You mean to tell me you will cut it open, just like this, without any anesthetic?" Vita demanded. "I can't allow it, doctor! This is barbaric. We are not living in the Middle Ages for God's sake. Can't you take her to the hospital? I demand to see the commandant!"

Vita marched out of the barracks and headed for the commandant's office with Helman right behind her. She pounded on the door. Vanya opened it.

"I want to see the commandant, now! It's very important!"

"He is not available. Go back to your barracks and be quiet!"

The inner door opened.

"What is going on here?" the man said.

"Igor Ivanovich, I have a very sick child. She needs surgery!"

"Oh, it's you!" He remembered her and their staring sessions during the meetings. "Vanya, let them in. Good evening, doctor." He turned to Helman, "What is it?"

"Well, Comrade, Mrs. Kew's daughter developed a boil on her forearm and it needs lancing and I...."

Vita was dumbfounded by Helman's meek attitude.

"This is unheard of! This is inhumane treatment! I will not allow my child to be carved up here, under these conditions!" She was now so enraged she could not control herself. "You mark my words, Igor Ivanovich, the League of Nations will hear about it one day!"

"I am shaking in my boots," he replied. "Doctor, how bad is it?" He turned to Helman.

"Well, the boil has to be lanced."

"Can't you do it here?"

"I don't have any anesthetic. It could be quite painful."

The commandant's wife walked into the office.

"Iggy, may I see you for a moment?"

He walked out with her, closing the door behind them.

"You are a spineless ninny," Vita turned on Helman. "You are afraid of your own shadow."

"Mrs. Kew, you are upset. You won't get anywhere creating this sort of commotion."

"Oh, no? We will see about that!"

The commandant's wife was motioning to Vita to come into her quarters. Vita shot Helman a murderous glance and followed her in.

"My name is Valeria Yevgenovna. Please sit down. I overheard you out there. Your daughter needs surgery? I am sure Igor Ivanovich will do all he can to help." She was very soft spoken and seemed genuinely concerned.

"Yes, Valeria Yevgenovna, can you imagine cutting on a child's arm without an anesthetic? Would you allow that on your children?"

She now had an opportunity and she was not going to let it pass without telling this woman everything she had been rehearsing over and over for some time. With tears in her eyes she unburdened her soul. How they were taken by mistake; they were Swiss citizens; her husband was a diplomat; they were just visitors; they didn't belong here. She went on and on. Valeria Yevgenovna put her hand on Vita's arm.

"I will see what I can do. I have two small children myself. I understand how a mother feels. You can come and talk to me anytime you want to."

Vita thanked her profusely. When she finally left, Helman was nowhere to be seen. She ran to her barracks with new hope and a great sense of accomplishment. She did it! She won! She didn't care about anybody else. She and Ellie would surely benefit from this. Ellie was in tears when she got to their room.

"Oh, Mother, am I glad to see you. I was so worried. Dr. Helman told me you created quite a scene. I was sure you were arrested!"

Vita hugged her daughter, holding her for a long time.

"Everything is fine, sweetheart, don't you worry. There are times when we have to be brave and strong and take a chance. I was scared, but I just had to do it!"

****

Helman took Ellie into Beresnik the next day. When they got back, Ellie's arm was bandaged with a real gauze bandage and it was in a sling.

"Mother, you should have seen it. When they lanced the boil, the pus squirted all over everything! It was disgusting!"

"Ellie, please...." Vita cupped her hand over her mouth.

"And it hurt a lot, even though they sprayed it with something cold beforehand."

She unwrapped a small package she had brought back: an extra bandage, some gauze squares, and a small envelope with a few sulfa pills.

"I am supposed to take these twice a day. Dr. Helman will change the dressing for me. I should heal soon."

"I am sorry, Mrs. Kew," Helman said sheepishly. "You were right, as usual. I guess I am not as brave as you are."

"No, you are not! Shame on you! You are supposed to be a man!"

****

Valeria Yevgenovna, wife of Captain Igor Ivanovich Smolensky, had a story of her own to tell. Lacking adult companionship, she welcomed an occasional visit from the Swiss lady. They spent an hour together when Vita brought her a small gift as a token of her gratitude for intervening on her behalf. Ellie's small gold and coral earrings were just the right thing for the commandant's eight-year-old daughter. Valeria Yevgenovna loved them and accepted them graciously.

She was a very intelligent, well-educated young woman who, once upon a time, aspired to a ballet career. That dream faded away when she married a young NKVD officer and had two children a year and a half apart.

When, for some unknown reason, her husband fell out of favor with the Communist Party and was punished by this degrading assignment in Siberia, she chose to stand by him and accompany him to this labor camp in Vozemka. He was angry and bitter with his party, but he was devoted to his wife. Valeria Yevgenovna made many sacrifices, and he was beholden to her. She had made the best out of their situation, never complaining, never regretting her decision. They were together and that mattered the most. He adored the ground she walked on. Privately, he called her "Dushka" — a little soul. He also understood and condoned her infrequent visits with that rebellious Swiss lady.

"Iggy, I need to occasionally have a woman-to-woman conversation above the eight-year-old level. You don't mind, do you?" she implored. "I can also brush up on my French, which I have almost completely forgotten. You know, she is quite a remarkable woman. Imagine, being separated from her husband and taken up here just because she happened to be in the wrong place at the wrong time. I really admire her spunk."

"Wait a minute, she was going to report me to the League of Nations, remember?"

"I know, but she was desperate — I would have done the same thing."

"What, reported me too?" he teased her.

"No, silly, insisted my child be taken to a hospital."

"Well, we have to be careful not to show any favoritism among these people."

****

Summer was ending. Rumors of a large shipment of goods spread like wildfire among the prisoners. Nobody knew any details, but at that week's meeting they were told winter clothing had arrived and would be distributed to the workers.

"Stachanoviets" and children get the first choice, they were told. The shop clerk was busy arranging piles of strange-looking, dark gray clothes while long lines formed in front of the store. The group was all there. When it was their turn, Vita and Ellie were handed two pairs of pants and jackets called "fufaykas," one large square wool head scarf for Vita and a man's quilted hat with ear flaps for Ellie, and two pairs of "valanky." Those were the strangest looking boots any of them had ever seen.

"Ladies, remember, don't pick a size smaller than your feet," teased Wozniak.

They carried their "wardrobes" to their rooms to try them on.

The pants and jackets were made out of a cotton shell quilted in two inch wide, vertical lines and stuffed with something soft, probably wool. The "valanky" boots were made out of three-quarter inch thick, felt-like wool fabric, molded into a boot shape, without any seams. Ellie put hers on, giggling and walking stiff-legged across the room. They came up several inches above her knees.

"How do you wear them? I can't bend my legs!" She marched down the hallway to the Kucharskis; and when she came back, she was full of information.

"You cut the tops off, Mother, and save the pieces; and when the bottoms wear out, you make soles out of the pieces and sew them on. Isn't that clever?"

"Wonderful," said Vita. "What ever happened to leather?"

"Well, I suppose these are warmer."

****

The light work they were enjoying for a while was over, and the group was shifted back to their regular, back-breaking hard labor. The weather was changing. It seemed as though the days were not quite as bright. Billows of fog hovered over the marshy areas and a fine drizzle persisted days at a time. Only very heavy downpours excused the workers from trudging into the woods and putting in their regular hours of labor. Unfortunately, there were just a few of those as most of the heavy rains fell at night.

Ellie answered the knock on her door and let Anya in. Vita was visiting the commandant's wife. She had made a very pretty jumpsuit for Valeria Yevgenovna's little girl out of the bright calico fabric she had left over and had taken it to her.

"Gees, you're all wet. What have you been doing out in this rain?" asked Ellie.

"I have been walking out there, thinking. I decided to talk to the doctor. Will you come with me? Please? This is the second period I have missed, and I just have to know."

"Sure, I will," Ellie said awkwardly. "I could get him right now. Mother won't be back for a while." She ran down the hallway and knocked on the doctor's door.

"Dr. Helman, could you please come over to my room; Anya would like to talk to you."

Helman was sleeping. Ellie felt guilty, robbing him of the few hours of rest he managed to get.

"What is it, Ellie? Is it an emergency?" His sleepy voice came through the door.

"No, but I think it's very important."

"All right, I will be right there."

"He is coming, Anya," she told the girl, closing the door behind her.

She let the doctor in, latching the door behind him.

"What's the problem, girls? My, you look like a drowned rat, Anya," he smiled at the rain-soaked girl.

"Anya wants to ask you a few questions, doctor. I will go outside and watch the door." She waited out in the hallway for the longest time. Finally the door opened and Helman motioned her to come in. Anya was sitting on the edge of the cot crying and laughing at the same tim, pitifully, her hands covering her face.

"She is pregnant, Ellie," he said matter-of-factly. "I am quite sure."

"I don't want it. I want to get rid of it. Please, doctor, you have got to help me!" Anya was sobbing. "And I don't want anybody to know about it — especially my mother!"

"Now, just a minute, young lady. Your mother is the first one I have to talk to."

"NO!" she screamed. "You don't know her. Oh, I wish I were dead!"

Ellie sat down beside her friend, her arm around her shoulders. She looked up at Helman, tears streaming down her face.

"What are we going to do?"

"It's up to her, but her mother has to know."

"Anya," he put his hand on her head. "I will tell her if you can't; she may take it from me."

"Oh, she hates you, just like she hates all the other Jews."

"Well, that's beside the point. Right now she has no other choice...I am it. You let me know what you decide, but don't wait too long, okay?"

The girls sat there for a while, miserable and weepy.

"Let him talk to her," Ellie finally said.

"I guess I will have to because I just can't face her. You don't know how mean she can be."

****

At the end of that week, the matter was settled. Mrs. Karowska took the news with icy calm. She was going to report the "rape" to the commandant and have that guard, whom she had suspected for a long time, arrested and punished.

"Oh, Mrs. Karowska. I wouldn't do that," Helman warned her. "That is not the story I got from Anya. Why don't you talk to her about it. She really needs a friend now."

"I have nothing to say to her. I want you to take care of the messy situation as quietly as possible. And I thank you very much."

"Oh, you miserable bitch," Helman mumbled to himself.

****

There was an outbreak of some kind of flu or grippe throughout the camp. A garden-variety under normal conditions but, in Vozemka, the undernourished, weak prisoners succumbed to it in great numbers. Helman spent all of his evening and night hours visiting the sick and distributing small doses of quinine to those with high fever.

"Will it do any good?" asked Ellie, his faithful helper.

"Well, it can't do any harm. Besides I don't have anything else."

He was exhausted. His clothes hung loosely on his bony frame and the thin, hollow face said it all. He knew he could not keep up this pace any longer, but he also could not ignore the sick and the dying. His wife, Sarah, was almost in a catatonic state now and needed as much attention as a small child. He blessed Mrs. Kos who took such good care of her and the children during the days, but at night he was on his own. A man could endure only so much, and he realized he was at an end of his strength, physically and mentally.

Ellie watched him standing there, deep in thought, automatically tying a cloth over his mouth and nose, ready to go into another bunkhouse.

"You got the grippe too?" she asked. "You look sick."

"No, I am just tired. Let's quit here; it's late and I still have to take Sarah and the children to the bathhouse. I also wanted to tell you that Anya is all right now. It is all over. She was one scared little girl. You are a good friend, and she is very grateful for your help and support. She has no one else."

"So, it's all done? Are you sure she will be all right?"

"Yes, she is fine. Mrs. Karowska wants this to stay just between the four of us, Ellie."

"Yes, I know. I didn't even tell my mother."

****

The flu and pneumonia killed several elderly Jews, and they were swiftly transported to the village for burial. Dr. Helman had a long conference with the commandant. He was too meek and fearful to demand anything, but he hoped to appeal to the man's humane side. He didn't get anywhere. Igor Ivanovitch listened, made a few notes, even sympathized with the doctor's plight, but he had no way to obtain medication for the entire camp, nor did he intend to relieve Helman of his woodcutting labor to take care of the sick and injured exclusively. It was up to him to volunteer his help. He was not required to do it.

"But Igor Ivanovitch, I can't, as a doctor, just close my eyes and ignore the people who need me."

"It's up to you!" And that was that.

****

September, 1940. Autumn in Siberia. The change in weather was at first imperceptible, but it was definitely there, with its cooler nights, falling leaves and drizzly, gray days. And the mushrooms! They sprung up all over the woods in clusters of several different varieties. Some were bright yellow, some had large brown meaty heads, some grew close to the ground, reddish in color with a flat, wide crown. Protein! The prisoners would gather them during their lunch breaks, eating them raw or roasting them in the open fire on long skewers.

"Just make sure they are not poisonous," warned Helman. Marta Kucharska was the group's expert.

"These are the best, in my opinion," she would say, pointing to the large, brown-headed variety. They are "prawdziwki". "They have wonderful texture and taste and can also be dried over the stove and preserved for the winter. Those are rydze," she explained, picking up the reddish kind. "If you cut through the stem, you will notice a red ring, and the stem is supposed to be hollow. These are very good to preserve in brine, just like pickles. But be careful, there are several 'imitators' very similar and very poisonous!"

Vita devised her own different methods of cooking them and incorporating them into their daily diet. They made a wonderful addition to the barley soup she cooked with her extra portions of kasha or just broiled on the hot iron stove top and sprinkled with a little salt. And when the top of it cooled down, just before she went to bed, she would cover it with slices of the drying variety. She had to collect them in the morning when the fire was rekindled, but as soon as the stove top cooled down sufficiently, she would lay them out again, turning them over. It took sometimes several nights for the slices to dry completely, but the result was well worthwhile.

One day while searching for berries in the woods, the girls came upon a curious-looking vine all entwined around a young sapling tree, its tendrils pulling on the branches, choking it visibly. Yet the vine was covered with beautiful clusters of grape-like fruit, big and round, ready to pick.

"Look at this," Anya pointed to the fruit. "How beautiful and large the berries are. We could gather a bucketful in no time."

They filled their containers and ran home to show off their newly-found harvest. Marta Kucharska was first to examine the over-flowing buckets.

"Oh no, girls, don't touch these. They are terribly poisonous," she exclaimed.

"But they are so pretty," argued Ellie.

"Sure they are pretty, but also deadly. The flowers smell of dead flesh and the berries are poisonous. Throw them out right now!"

"Oh, you found the carrion vine." Wozniak looked at it with interest. I didn't know it grew this far north."

"There is a lot of it in the woods, but Mrs. Kucharska says it's no good," Anya said visibly disappointed.

"Well, let me tell you about it," said Wozniak, forever the teacher. "It's an unusual vine. It's so lovely, so showy. The flowers and fruit are beautiful, but the tendrils spread and stifle the life of everything in their path. You could almost compare it to the communist system. Beautiful ideals, perfect theory, but insidious and deadly in real life. Oh, yes, the carrion vine, how very interesting."

The girls left him standing there, deep in thought, fingering the fruit, a curious expression on his face.

With the rainy season in full force, the dirt roads leading to the village of Vozemka from Beresnik were often impassable with food supply trucks bogged down days at a time. Consequently, trips on the wooden rails between the village and the camp were infrequent, if any, as there were no supplies to be brought up.

For Vita's group, the cooked berries, mushrooms and other food items that Jan Wozniak kept trading for with the Russian stachanoviets, the store keeper and the cook, were life savers, supplementing the meager rations of food. Some days, when staples were low, only the watery soup would be provided for the workers at noon and the usual "zahvtrah" (tomorrow) was offered instead of their evening meals.

Hunger is a word that has absolutely no meaning to those who have never experienced it. It is a nagging, persistent, ever-present gut ache that has a strange effect on the human body and mind. It brings out the worst in men's character; one would do almost anything for a scrap of food. Normally decent men would stoop so low as to steal rations from the weak and sick, from small children and old women. Dr. Helman despaired.

"We will lose everybody if we don't get some decent food up here," he whined to the commandant.

"As soon as the ground freezes, transports will start coming up again on a regular basis," he was told.

"But, Igor Ivanovitch, starvation reaches a point of no return. No amount of food will bring these people back; it will be too late!"

And for hundreds of them it was.

Truckload after truckload rolled down the wooden rails carrying dozens of skeleton-like bodies to be disposed of somewhere in the village. The prayers and keening of relatives and companions could be heard throughout the camp daily.

The group stuck together, helping one another, sharing what little food there was and, above all, keeping clean. Vita was in charge of the group's "hygiene." She prodded, she nagged, until all her charges would run out of excuses and follow her to the bathhouse regularly. Ellie was no exception.

"I'm too tired, Mother. Can't I go tomorrow?"

"No, tomorrow is the men's night. Come on, come on, you will feel so much better."

Ellie lifted her tired body off the cot and resignedly followed her, joining the other women.

"Mrs. Kew, my mother can't come tonight. Her lumbago is worse," Anya reported.

"Oh, that's too bad, but I am sure the steam would do her good."

"She just won't go. She can't get off her bed. Dr. Helman told her to rest."

It was always a chore to get them to go, but they all later admitted how much better their aching bodies felt and how well they slept after those steam baths.

There are leaders and there are followers. Vita was a born leader, an organizer and a clear thinker. Her mind was never at rest. She decided at the onset of this dilemma she found herself in that she would survive and so would her daughter. She realized the odds were against them, but she would not give up. She reminded herself of that resolve over and over, writing it down in her little diary: We shall get out of this hellish place one day...we shall make it...we shall survive!

****

15

THE LONG RUSSIAN WINTER

*...She would have to be very careful
with her cheating routine, but she also knew she had to continue,
or figure out some other way to fulfill their quota.
The food, as meager as it was, was essential to their survival
and to lose it would have been disastrous...*

Season changes in Siberia are quite timely and definite. By October the temperatures fall considerably, and November welcomes its first snowfalls, light at the beginning, then consistently heavier and, by the end of the month, the snow is knee deep with temperatures falling from -30° to -50°.

This winter was no exception. The only redeeming factor for the "lumberjacks," working their regular eight-hour shifts, was the complete stillness of the air. There was practically no movement, no breeze. In the total quiet one could hear a twig snap a mile away. The snow was powdery and dry; and if it were not a place of drudgery and backbreaking work, one could feast one's eyes on the beauty of the land and the ancient, magnificent forests.

But the laborers' attention was centered on more mundane tasks, like keeping their feet and hands from freezing. Noses, cheeks and chins were constantly threatened by frostbite. It happened fast, without warning; a cheek or nose would turn white and lose its feeling and, in time, if left alone, would necrotize and fester. Some rubbed their faces with rough mittens at regular intervals; others would wrap wool scarves around their faces right up to their eyes. Breathing and sight were impaired, but skin was protected and, with the warming breaks at the bonfires, frostbite was held down to a minimum.

Feet were another matter. The workers who had earned their winter clothing would wrap newspaper scraps around their feet over their socks for extra insulation and slip them into the felt "valanky." The ones who did not get any clothing tied their own worn shoes with layers of rags to protect their toes.

Helman, during his rest periods, ran from group to group, checking, instructing and helping the ones most vulnerable, older men in particular.

"Move around, wiggle your toes, shake your arms," he shouted at the tired, lethargic laborers.

Some listened to him; others did not care. There was so much frostbite among them that by the time winter was in full force, many gangrenous toes had to be snipped off, maiming the men for life. Helman made numerous trips to Beresnik with the more serious cases; the others he treated right there, in his little "office."

The large supply of atabrine proved useful after all. It was supposed to treat malaria in conjunction with quinine, but it also was a potent disinfectant. Helman would make a strong solution, dissolving the yellow pills in boiling water. He would wash all the wounds, boil bandages and instruments in it. It also proved to be a powerful dye. Some of the dingy, grayish sweaters or shirts, dunked in an atabrine bath, turned bright yellow!

****

"Mother, why don't the Russians celebrate Christmas?" Ellie wondered.

"The old, white Russians did. It used to be as big a holiday as ours; but when the Communists took over, they closed all the churches and banned all religious celebrations."

"How odd. I can't imagine what it would be like to have the government enforce such rules on the people."

"Well, Ellie, we were lucky to be born in a country that's very democratic. As long as we pay taxes and obey the law, we can do almost anything we want to!"

****

Christmas came and went without any change of the work routine; but, within the group, quietly they gathered late at night and, following an old Polish custom, broke bread and embraced, wishing each other better fortune and hoping to spend their next Christmas at home. There were tears and dejection, hope and speculation, but above all a feeling of unity and friendship. They had become a family of sorts, and it gave them strength to survive. Anya tearfully hugged Ellie, whispering thanks into her ear. Even Mrs. Karowska, usually aloof and standoffish, shook hands with the others, obviously too emotional to speak. They parted with a feeling of solidarity and a resolve to endure.

****

The news spread fast through the barracks. Sarah Helman was dead! They found her sitting in the snow, propped up against a tree, not fifty feet from the buildings, frozen to death. She evidently slipped out of her room quietly and unnoticed, wearing nothing but her night clothes. She either could not, in her confused state, find her way back or, in a moment of sanity, chose to end it all. The speculations were never answered.

"It's really a blessing," someone volunteered. "She was here in body only, her mind was dead long ago."

They all rallied around the doctor and the children, offering sympathy and support. He was loved and admired by many people for all the help and concern he showed them. He was a good man. Ellie felt a lot more sorrow and pity for her friend than all the others, but she didn't quite know what to say or what to do. He knew how she felt, looking at her troubled face and teary eyes.

They buried Sarah the next day. Helman was allowed to take her into the village, a concession by the commandant, not usually given to other families.

Death under any circumstances is a grim, devastating occurrence; and it always saddens even though for some it seems to be an angel of mercy. Suicides, on the other hand, are quite a different phenomenon. The reaction, at first, is a shocked disbelief, then a feeling of wonderment. Why? What was the reason? Then comes anger and resentment. It's a selfish, cruel act without regard for the ones left behind. It is unforgivable — a sign of weakness and moral disintegration. There is a stigma attached to it that leaves the survivors with a feeling of guilt and shame.

Camp Vozemka wasn't any different. Sarah Helman seemed to have pointed a way to an easy end to all the misery, suffering and degradation. The "white death," as the Russians called it, was painless and clean. All one had to do was walk out into the night, find a quiet resting place, and fall asleep. That was all there was to it. Or was it?

After several such deaths — some entire families — Helman took it upon himself to spend every moment of his free time helping others. It was a one-man crusade. The others in the group felt no such responsibility. Every one of them fought a battle for his own survival, and the ones who had given up hope of ever winning it, well, that was their choice. Not much sympathy was wasted on them.

Vita and Ellie argued about it hours on end, but their main concern was the doctor's own health. He seemed to be driven by some inner strength or guilt and no amount of persuasion on the part of Wozniak and Stan Kucharski or Vita had any effect on him.

"You have got to think of your own children," Vita would argue. "They need you more than all the other strangers!"

"They are well taken care of and, besides, remember our pact? If anything ever happens to either one of us, the survivor takes over. They will be in good hands!"

She gave up.

****

There was no rhyme or reason in the way the work was assigned to the different groups of prisoners. Some days they put up their cubic meters of logs, other days they stripped branches and bark off of the long straight trunks of trees; and when the birch "truck fuel" supply was low, they gladly switched to the lighter work.

They now had a new guard. Anya's friend served his term at the camp and was called into the army. Vita eyed the new man with apprehension. He was much older and quite surly. She would have to be very careful with her cheating routine, but she also knew she had to continue or figure out some other way to fulfill her and Ellie's quota. The food, as meager as it was, was essential to their survival and to lose it would have been disastrous.

She might try to bribe him, but she would have to be very clever not to get caught. She fished a large, gold man's watch out of her fast-dwindling cache of trinkets and strapped it to her wrist. Whenever the guard stopped by, she would flash it in front of him to check the time. The temptation was too great for him to resist.

"That's a pretty big watch for a woman to wear," he commented one day.

"It's my husband's," she lied. "It's pure gold, you know. And it keeps time to the second. It's made in Switzerland."

He took the bait.

"Do you have another one?"

"Oh, yes, I have a smaller one, but I like this one the best." She smiled at him.

From that day on, he marked his log book without counting the stacked wood piles.

"You and your boy are good workers. I trust you," he would say checking them out. Vita handed him the watch. He slipped it into his pocket.

Ellie moved away from them pretending not to see. One of these days she will get caught, she thought, scared out of her wits.

"You know, Mother, you could go to jail for this."

"Sure, but so could he. Don't worry, he will not report me. He now knows I have other things his little black heart might desire."

With that she sat down on a tree trunk and lit up a cigarette. It was the last smidgeon of tobacco she had, but she felt she deserved a treat!

****

Vanya handed Vita a small piece of paper. It was a note from Valeria Yevgenovna asking her to stop by on Saturday. Vita put the note into her fufayka pocket and in her mind went over the list of things she had been planning to bring up during their next visit.

****

"Meeting" nights were additional drudgery for the prisoners to endure. Exhausted after a long day's labor, they were required to attend and spend over an hour listening to the chief supervisor's propaganda speeches: the Sovietski Soyuz was the biggest power in the world; its army was the best trained and equipped force; the communist leaders were all distinguished heroes; all the satellite countries, once taken away, were now coming back to "Mother Russia."

Wozniak's attention perked up. He exchanged glances with the others. What satellite countries were back under Russian rule besides Poland, he wondered. Being cut off from the world, not knowing what was going on in Europe, how the war was progressing, was the most frustrating, maddening thing to endure. There just had to be a way to find out. But how? His bartering meetings with the Russian stachanoviets were short and clandestine. He slipped them a piece of jewelry, and they handed over a sack of potatoes. There was no time to chat about anything. Besides, Wozniak was quite sure the same stupid propaganda that was fed to the general Russian public wasn't any different from what they heard at the camp. And Bernie Helman was such a ninny, he thought. He had the opportunities, he went to Beresnik, he had contact with the doctors out there, but he was afraid of his own shadow.

"Come on, Jan," his wife was tugging at his sleeve, "the meeting is over."

****

"What was your father's name?" Valeria Yevgenovna asked Vita, handing her a cup of tea.

"Alexander Cressimon."

"Oh, well, from now on then, I shall call you Vita Alexandrovna. We always use our first names with the names of our fathers. Anyway, the reason I asked you to come to see me is this awful coat my husband bought me. It's much too big, but it's so nice and warm and it's a Vicuna. I would like to be able to use it. Can you do something to make it fit me?"

Vita looked the garment over carefully.

"I certainly can try. Here, put it on. Let's see what we can do."

She tucked the long sleeves under, pinned up the hem about a foot, and folded a big pleat in the back.

"I think it will fit much better now. I might even make you a matching hat out of the remnants," she said.

"You do such beautiful work. Were you a seamstress?"

"Oh, no. It's just my hobby. I have always loved to sew."

"I have a small sewing machine you are welcome to use," offered Valeria Yevgenovna, pointing to an antiquated hand-cranked model.

"That's wonderful. I will put it all together for you to try on and then I will sew it up on the machine. It will go much faster," she said.

Vita looked forward to more trips to the commandant's house. She didn't have a chance to talk further to Valeria Yevgenovna. The commandant brought the children back from a sleigh ride, and it was time for their lessons. But she would be back!

****

January, 1941. "What have we here?"

Helman was looking Ellie over with great concern. She was obviously feverish and complained of aches and pains in her hands, elbows and knees, and had a sore throat. Her knuckles were swollen to double their size.

"All my joints hurt and they feel so hot inside. What is it, Dr. Helman?"

"I am not sure, but I hope to God it isn't rheumatic fever. It certainly looks like it. We will watch it for a couple of days. I will speak to the commandant. We will have to get some salicylates from the hospital. It's the only thing that will reduce the inflammation and bring the fever down."

"How long will this last?" Ellie wanted to know.

"I don't know, but you stay in bed and keep warm."

He walked out of the room with Vita right behind him.

"If this is what I think it is, it's a very serious disease. Let's hope hers is a light case and the damage is not serious."

"What damage? What do you mean?" Vita frantically asked.

"Well, it sometimes scars the heart valves."

"Oh, God! Shouldn't she be in a hospital?"

"Now, don't panic. If I get the medication, she will be fine right here. They can't do much more for her than we can. I will ask the commandant to let you stay home for a few days to take care of her. I don't want her up and around any more than is absolutely necessary. And above all, keep smiling. I don't want her worrying about something that might not happen."

He left her standing there devastated and close to tears, but it took just a moment to pull herself together and enter the room with a bright smile on her face. The girl was anxiously looking up at her, her cheeks flushed, her eyes wide open.

"So what's the verdict? Am I going to die?"

"Oh, no, no such luck! You are going to live and suffer with the rest of us! Seriously though, Dr. Helman says it sometimes can be bad, but he hopes yours is a light case, and he will do his best to get some medicines for you from the hospital, and I will ask for a few days off so that I can take care of you. It will give me a nice rest too. You are supposed to stay in bed at all times and keep warm."

She stoked the piechka and put some water on to boil. She then sat down by the window and ripped the seams of Valeria Yevgenovna's coat.

By evening the news of Ellie's illness brought the group, one by one, inquiring, commiserating, offering help. Stan Kucharski piled a large stack of firewood and kindling outside Vita's door. Mrs. Kos asked if she could help take care of Ellie. Jan Wozniak came to see her, promising to barter for some sugar. Anya spent part of the evening chatting and keeping Ellie's spirits up. Vita was overwhelmed and thankful.

Helman apparently did a good job presenting his case to the commandant. He got a written requisition for the medication and permission for Vita to stay home with her daughter. He was gone most of the next day but came back empty-handed. The hospital was out of salicylates, and it would take several days to get a supply shipped to Vozemka. He brought a large bottle of aspirin which, he explained, contained some salicylic acid, but not in large enough doses to control the inflammation. Every afternoon Vita ran out to meet the mail runner returning from the village with the camp's mail.

"Neechevo, sievodnya (nothing today)," he informed her.

Finally on the sixth day, he had a package addressed to Dr. Helman from the Beresnik hospital. Both Helman and Vita were not quite sure whether the salicylates helped or the disease just ran its course, but after two or three weeks the swelling went down considerably, the fever dropped, and Ellie started to feel a little better.

"That's a tough little girl we've got here," he told Vita after examining Ellie's knuckles, wrists and knees. "It could have been much worse."

Vita sent word through Vanya that Valeria Yevgenovna's coat was ready for her to try. It was all cut down and basted and started to look rather smart. The reply came back almost immediately. "Please come tomorrow," the note said.

"How is your daughter?" Valeria Yevgenovna wanted to know as soon as Vita entered the house.

"She is much better, and I do want to thank you very much for the tea and sugar you sent over for her. She really enjoyed it. That was awfully kind of you."

"Believe me, it was nothing. I wish I could have done more. It's just an awkward situation we are in here, and Igor Ivanovitch can't very well...."

"Please, you don't have to explain. I understand. Here, try this on. Let's see what it looks like."

Valeria Yevgenovna slipped the coat on and an expression of total amazement lit up her face.

"How on earth did you ever do this? It doesn't look anything like the old coat, and it fits me perfectly! It's incredible!"

"I will sew it up on your machine and then finish it by hand," said Vita handing her a smart-looking toque-like hat. The woman's mouth fell open. She ran to a small mirror and put it on over her dark hair which was pulled back into a large bun. The hat fit her perfectly.

"Vita Alexandrovna! I don't know what to say. How will I ever repay you for this?"

You will, thought Vita, smiling at her.

"I was glad to do it," she finally said. "I had the time, not having to work while my daughter was ill. I actually enjoyed doing something like this for a change. Wouldn't you say my talents were wasted out there in the woods?"

There was an awkward moment of silence.

"Well, I better be going."

"Thank you again, very much!" Valeria Yevgenovna walked her to the door.

****

Ellie was up and around but still staying indoors. The swelling in her hands and knees was gone, but it was still painful to use the joints and Helman didn't want her out in the bitter cold for any length of time. She was bored. There was nothing to do, nothing to read. She kept the fire going and did some cooking under Vita's supervision. After dinner Anya would stop by and amuse her with stories and comments about the outside world.

"When will you be well enough to get out?" Anya asked.

"I am ready now. I am tired of sitting here day after day, but Dr. Helman wants me out of the cold for a few more days. Can you believe this? I would rather go to work than be cooped up here!"

"No, I can't," answered Anya. "I would give anything to have a few days to myself."

****

"January is the coldest month up here," the local Russians would tell the prisoners. "There should be a break in the weather come February."

The temperatures hovered between -40°C and -50°C, and the number of prisoners still being able to put in a day's labor in the woods decreased daily at an alarming rate. The "no work — no food" slogan shouted at them during their weekly meetings was a threat strong enough for most of them to go out into the bitter cold just to be able to collect their ration of food at the end of the day. But for many, the effort was impossible. Physically and emotionally spent, the food was no longer enough of an incentive. There was no hope anymore; they were going to perish anyway, so what was the point.

The group knit together into one close family. Wozniak and Kucharski made nightly visits to each room, checking on every adult and child, sharing extra food, scraps of newspaper, repairing worn valanky, but mostly giving support, encouraging and keeping their spirits up. Vita continued her effort, not always successfully, with the bathhouse routine. Some nights it was too cold even for her to make that trip. The rooms remained snug and warm by keeping the fire going at all times. Mrs. Kos would feed the piechkas during the working hours. Ellie was back on the work force. Mercifully, they were again replenishing the truck fuel, so the work was relatively light. She made a valiant effort to keep up with the others.

****

16

SPRING 1941

In May 1941, London was subjected to one of its heaviest raids by the German Luftwaffe. Hundreds of buildings were destroyed. Germany prepared to attack the Soviet Union.

They were all praying for spring. But when it came, so did the thaws and the mud and the sporadic food shipments. Vita gathered enough courage to ask Valeria Yevgenovna for food. She desperately needed to supplement the scant portions of kasha and bread to keep her and Ellie's strength up. She got a bag of rice, some flour and a bottle of oil. That night she cooked up some flat pancakes and shared them with the others.

The frustration over not knowing what was happening in the world made one take chances with grave consequences. The strict order not to fraternize with the Russian inmates or hold clandestine meetings among themselves was, on the surface, observed by most of Vita's group. But somehow, somewhere small items of news filtered through and were passed along in spite of the constant threat of severe punishment.

"Germany is winning the war on all fronts! France and the Netherlands surrendered! It's spreading to the Near East!"

Those blood-curdling scraps of news were passed along among the prisoners with lightning speed.

"Could it be possible? Is Hitler strong or mad enough to spread his fronts over such vast territory? Or is it just propaganda?" wondered Helman. He was wrapping Jan Wozniak's sprained knee and listening to the newest bits of information.

"Bernie, you have got to get your hands on a newspaper when you go to Beresnik next time. I don't care how you do it. I can't stand this any longer. Or talk to the doctors; they should know what's going on!"

Helman moved his head up and down. "I will try."

Vita wondered about Paul. Where was he? What was he doing? Was Switzerland involved? It was unlikely, but as mad as Hitler seemed to be, anything was possible. Were they really doomed to spend the rest of their lives up here? The world seemed to be falling apart. Was there any chance of them ever returning to normal life? She spent sleepless nights fighting the doubts and fears, but come morning she got up with new resolve to survive, if not for her sake, then for her daughter's. Ellie deserved to have a life.

****

Official mail for the commandant's office and other small personal items were hand-carried by a mail runner who walked the ten kilometers to and from the village post office carrying a large knapsack-like pouch. This was the most coveted job, and it was usually assigned to an older Russian man or woman who had proven themselves to be good, steady workers. It was a reward of sorts. So when it was offered to Ellie, it came as a shock to the entire group, including Vita and her astonished daughter.

"What did you have to do to buy that?" Helman wanted to know.

"Believe me, I am just as surprised as you!" Vita retorted.

"I bet!"

Even Ellie questioned her, feeling awkward to be singled out and given this relatively easy job while the others slaved on in the woods. She was to start as soon as the present mail carrier left the camp, his term coming to an end.

A pair of leather, laced-up work boots came with that job and a regular ration of food tokens as well. Vita was delighted. Ten kilometers was not that long a distance to walk, she reasoned. Occasionally a truck made a return trip to the village in the mornings, rather than in the afternoons, and perhaps she could beg a ride on it. The commandant also kept a horse for his own occasional trips to the village or to Beresnik. She was already scheming how to approach Valeria Yevgenovna to make that chore as light as possible for Ellie. She was sure the commandant was influenced greatly by his wife, and she planned to take full advantage of that.

Survival! That was the uppermost goal of all her thoughts, all her actions. She was already carefully choosing a handsome gift for Valeria Yevgenovna out of her cache of jewelry.

Her first trips to the village were to be made with the present mail runner who was an older stachanoviet by the name of Meesha. He was to show Ellie what the job was all about.

"Don't wear the new boots, Ellie," warned her mother. "They look awfully hard and uncomfortable. You should break them in first."

They left in the morning just after Vanya handed them a packet of the commandant's mail to be delivered. Meesha had the mail runner's job for the past six months, and he liked to leave early so he could get back at a decent hour in the afternoon.

"You know, there are wolves around these woods, don't you?" he said.

"Yes, we hear them howling sometimes during the night. It's spine chilling."

Ellie's heart skipped a beat. Wolves! She had not given that a thought, and she had better not mention that little detail to her mother. She would probably create another scene at the commandant's office.

"Meesha, what do you do when you see the wolves?"

"Well, they are usually very cautious and they don't come too near, but they may follow you for awhile. They would have to get pretty hungry to attack, but you never know. It is just safer to walk during daylight."

"How long does it usually take you to get to the post office?"

"Oh, I normally allow two hours, sometimes more. You have to cross the river. The post office and most of the village is on the other side."

"A river? What do you do, swim?"

"No, there is a small boat and you row across. In the winter it freezes over, and you can walk on it, but you must be careful. You could break through."

Ellie was absorbing all the bits of information, getting more and more apprehensive about her new, seemingly "easy" job.

Meesha marched on one of the rails, singing in a loud voice. Ellie walked the other rail, trying to keep pace and checking her watch. They stopped twice to rest while Meesha smoked his stubby cigarette. He told her he was from the Ukraine and was sent to the labor camp for stealing food from the kolhoz he worked on. He didn't seem to be ashamed of it at all. Everybody did it, he explained. He was just unlucky to get caught. But his time was up and he was looking forward to getting back home.

"Are you married, and do you have children?" asked Ellie.

"Oh, yes. We have two grown sons. They are both in the army."

They were now approaching a small settlement. Several houses were clustered on a rise and the river could be seen down below. The largest part of the village was on the other side. The river was not very wide and, to Meesha's annoyance, both boats were pulled up on the other shore. He swore loudly, shouting to a pair of people standing next to the boats, talking. One of them waved back, pushed the boat into the water and started to row across. It was a small boat, maybe twelve feet long with a pair of attached oars.

"Zdrastvuitie, Meesha," he greeted the mail carrier. "I see you have a helper today. I didn't expect you this early." He smiled, handing the line to Meesha.

"Oh, you say that every time you hold that boat over there," he snapped, motioning Ellie to get in. She sat down on the furthest little bench while Meesha pushed off and grabbed the oars.

"Now remember, aim at the far tree on the other side. By the time you reach the shore, the current will move you right where you want to be, in front of the post office."

It looked easy enough. Ellie was sure she could handle it. They pulled the boat onto the shore and walked up a hill to a building with the red flag in front of it.

"This is the best part of this job," Meesha whispered to Ellie. "You can rest, have some kipiatok, read the paper, talk to the postmaster and then, if the mail is late, which it almost always is, you get to have lunch with the postmaster's family."

"You do?"

"Oh, yes. They are very nice and very helpful. You will see."

Ellie started to like this job a little better. Imagine, she thought, having lunch outside the camp, with a Russian family. I wonder what kind of food they have?

"The mail is late," the postmaster announced. "And there are two of you today?"

"Yes, this is Ellie, the new mail runner. I am going home."

"Well, good for you! How long were you in?"

"One year! Next month I'll be a free man!"

The postmaster eyed Ellie suspiciously. "You sure you can handle the job, boy? You look pretty weak. We will have to feed you up a bit!"

"I'll be fine, thank you." She didn't know whether to correct him, so she just let it pass and changed the subject.

"When do you think the mail will get here?" she asked.

"Oh, you never know, but it should be here soon. We will be eating in about half an hour, and you are welcome to join us."

"Oh, thank you very much."

Ellie could hardly wait. She sat down on one of the benches, looking at all the Red propaganda posters plastered around the walls. They depicted Russian soldiers planting red, flying flags in the center of maps of most of the Baltic countries, with huge titles saying, "Welcome back to your Mother Country." She tried to memorize all the names of the small nations now under the red flag. She would tell the group that night. It was not quite clear in her mind what it meant, but she was sure it was important information.

The midday meal was served in the postmaster's kitchen. He and his wife occupied a small house just down the street from the post office. There were six or seven people seated around the kitchen table waiting for the food to be brought in. The postmaster's wife placed two large wooden bowls in the center and handed each person a round wooden spoon. She then cut a thick, generous slice of white crusty bread and placed it on the well-scrubbed table in front of each person. It looked almost like cake and smelled unbelievably good. There were no plates or bowls to eat from, and Ellie wondered what a curious eating custom this was.

"Well, dig in!" said the postmaster, reaching with his spoon into the bowl full of borscht. He brought the spoon to his mouth, holding a small chunk of bread under it so it would not drip onto the table and slurped it, smacking his lips.

"Oh, that's good!" he said. "Go on, go on, eat," he urged Ellie who sat there not knowing what to do. All the other people took turns, dipping their spoons in the two communal bowls and then politely waiting their turn. Ellie, observing all the moves, finally helped herself to the soup and the mashed potatoes out of the second bowl. It was heaven, particularly the bread. She ripped it in half, saving the other half to take back to her mother. The postmaster's wife noticed that and, slicing another piece from the loaf, said to her, "Eat up, child. Here is a piece you can take with you."

Ellie's eyes filled with tears. All she could manage was a small "spaseebo" (thank you).

The lunch was interrupted by a loud horn sound coming from the river.

"The mail is here," said the postmaster, getting up and wiping his mouth with the back of his hand. Meesha handed him the packet he had brought from the camp, and they both walked down the embankment to meet the mail boat. It was a small, motor-powered craft with a canvas top operated by a single man. He tied up at the narrow pier, tossed out two bundles, picked up the mail from the camp and the village and was gone. The postmaster sorted out the items, tossing some of them into Meesha's pouch.

"Here is some tea for the commandant," he remarked, looking over a small, square tin and tossing it grudgingly into the pouch. "And tobacco. It's the commandant's brother who sends a lot of things to him. Books, clothes, children's toys — he is lucky to have a relative in a high position in Moscow."

The pouch all packed, Meesha was getting ready to head back.

"Here, you carry it," he said to Ellie. "Might as well get used to it." The walk back seemed much shorter. They spotted the camp buildings at the end of the road in no time at all.

****

"Look, Mother, see what I brought you!"

Vita was barely inside the room when Ellie grabbed her and hugged her.

"Close the door, Ellie. I see you liked your new job."

"Liked it? It was great! Here, you have got to try this bread right now!"

Vita instinctively hesitated.

"No, you eat it Ellie, you need it more than I do."

"Mother, I had a large piece with my lunch. If you don't eat it, I will not tell you anything more!"

"All right, put the water on, and let's also try one of our jams, shall we?"

Ellie kept prattling on and on, excitedly telling her about Meesha, the postmaster, his wife, the village, the posters in the post office.

"You know, we all ate out of the same dish?"

Vita made a face. "Really? How unsanitary!"

"I didn't care. Everything was so good, and you could eat as much as you wanted. I only wish I could have brought you some."

The ruby ring Vita selected for Valeria Yevgenovna, all of a sudden, was not good enough a gift for this latest favor. She must give her something more, something very nice, she thought, munching on the delicious bread.

****

By the end of the month, Ellie was a seasoned mail runner. At first, she had quite a problem crossing the river. Her first two or three attempts landed her way off her mark, the current moving the little boat downstream. She had to row very hard, almost at a 45 degree angle upstream, to land near the post office. She finally mastered it, her arms aching, her hands blistering.

The walk itself was routine. Some of the mornings she would meet the truck on its way to the camp. In the afternoons she met it again on its way back. Sometimes the walk was very lonely. The only sound came from the rhythmic pounding of her feet on the wooden rail. It reverberated through the silent woods, carried by an eerie echo. Ellie now understood why Meesha liked to sing during his walks. She tried it also. At first quietly, under her breath, then louder, and finally she would sing just like Meesha, her voice reverberating through the woods. Her favorite tune to march to was the Marseillaise. It had a great beat to it and she remembered all the words.

Some days she did a lot of thinking, mostly about her father and the hopeless situation she and her mother were in. Then she would work out elaborate plans of their escape. Maybe it could be done, maybe they could just walk out of the camp one night, follow the river to a large town, get lost in it, contact some friendly, non-communist Russians and with their help make it to a neutral country. But where? And how? She knew how hopeless those dreams were, but in her imagination she concocted a myriad of possibilities with the final wonderful end — her father walking toward them to greet and embrace them, like in a book or a movie!

****

Sorting the incoming mail was an easy task that Ellie willingly offered to do. She would run down to the pier, hand the outgoing mail to the boat man, and carry the small sack back to the post office.

"What have we got there today?" inquired the postmaster.

"Oh, not much — some letters, a small package and newspapers."

"Well, take yours and get going. It looks like a storm is coming."

Her heart pounding, she picked up two newspapers, rather than the customary one for the commandant, and put them in the bottom of her pouch. She tossed the rest in and placed the freshly baked loaf of bread gently on top. This was the day of the week that the postmaster's wife always sent a loaf to the commandant.

Well out of sight, on her way back, she fished out the extra newspaper and slid it under her jacket, tightening her belt around it. Then she almost ran home.

Vanya was there to greet her and collect the official camp mail, the bread for Valeria Yevgenovna, and a small stack of printed propaganda fliers he would distribute at the next meeting.

She was astonished to find her mother in their room, busy cooking something on the stove.

"Oh, Ellie, you will never guess what happened today! Valeria Yevgenovna kept her promise. I am no longer working in the woods! I am assigned to clean the Russians' bunk houses and the commandant's house! Isn't that wonderful?"

"How did you ever manage that, Mother? Or shouldn't I ask?"

"Just by being very clever and very nice," she answered smugly.

"Well, you are not the only one who is very, very clever." Ellie reached under her jacket. "Ta, da!" She brought the newspaper out and waved it in front of her mother's face. Vita couldn't believe her eyes. There was the entire "Izvyestya," not just year-old scraps to be used as boot wraps or cigarette paper, but a new, clean,

190

relatively recent newspaper.

"How on earth did you get that?"

"Well, I now sort the mail by myself, and there were more copies there today than normally, so I thought nobody would notice if one was missing. Can you imagine what Mr. Wozniak will say when he sees this?"

Vita was busily scanning the headlines, an expression of total disbelief on her face.

"Ellie, run down to Mrs. Kos's and ask her to tell Mr. Wozniak when he comes to pick up his girls to stop by this evening."

He came right after dinner, rapping quietly on their door.

"Is anything wrong?"

"No, no, on the contrary! Look what Ellie brought us!"

"What is it?"

"The entire 'Izvyestya' dated just a few days ago!"

He grabbed Ellie in a crushing bear hug and placed a resounding smack on her forehead.

"You are wonderful! I won't even ask how you did it, but I hope you can do it again!"

"I will try," she said with a grin.

They were both now engrossed in reading the different items on the front page.

"Look here, the British sunk the Bismarck! And look at this, the front spread to the Middle East. The British are in Basra! That's just a little south of the Russian border!" Wozniak excitedly flipped the pages, trying to absorb as much as possible.

"Here, you take half of the paper with you and read it all. I will do the same and then we can switch."

Vita needed some peace and quiet to digest all of this alone. He slid the folded paper under his shirt and slipped out of the room.

It was almost too much of a good thing for one day. She ran out of writing paper a long time ago, but she used the back sides of the propaganda fliers they were given at the meetings. Her writing was tiny and concise. There were huge gaps in her diary because of the lack of paper, so she crammed as much as she could on each page. Just the highlights...just the most important events.

****

She now saw Valeria Yevgenovna on a daily basis. As soon as she was through with the cleaning of the bunk houses, she rushed over to the commandant's house and helped his wife with her housework and the children. It was an easy job, and it had many advantages. The Russian stachanoviets had always more food. They had contacts in the village and could buy things like salted pork, farmer's white cheese, milk and potatoes. Vita bartered for some of the items with her practically exhausted supply of trinkets. Food and warm clothing were essential to their survival. She used all her energy and cunning toward that end.

****

"Mother, would it be all right if Anya stayed with us for awhile?" asked Ellie one day. "She had a terrible fight with her mother and Mrs. Karowska told her to leave."

"Leave? What do you mean leave? Where is she supposed to go?"

"That's just it. She has no place to go. Please, could she just bunk here with us?"

"I don't know, Ellie. I will have to ask Mrs. Karowska."

"I knew you would say that! All I want to do is help a friend. She is very unhappy. Her mother isn't very nice to her. Maybe if they were separated, they would get along better. Please?"

"Oh, all right, but just for a little while, until they settle their differences, but I do have to mention it to her mother."

"Thank you. I will tell Anya right away. She can move her things tonight. You will see, it will be fun having her here."

Vita shook her head. What on earth was the reason for this kind of breakup? She would have a talk with Greta very soon.

Anya moved her things into their room that night. She didn't have much — some clothes, her cot and bedding. She presented a sorry picture, sitting on her cot, crying quietly. Vita couldn't get over how beautiful the girl was. And so mature — physically, at least. She was only two years older than Ellie, but Ellie still looked like a child while Anya was a woman. It was amazing.

"Well, girls, I am off to the kitchen. Give me your food token Anya. I will pick up our dinner."

"I don't have one, Mrs. Kew. Mother wouldn't give it to me when I left. It's all right. I am not very hungry."

"No, it's not all right! But don't worry about it. I cooked some barley soup with dried mushrooms and some salt pork. There will be enough for all of us."

She walked out of the room angry and with a firm resolve to give Mrs. Karowska a piece of her mind. She didn't have to wait long for the opportunity. Greta met her outside the barrack's door and, in her own inimitable fashion, full of sarcasm and venom, thanked her for giving her daughter asylum.

"I don't know what your difficulties are," Vita said to her, "but I just don't think that throwing your child out of your home is an answer!"

"Oh, no? Well, let me tell you a thing or two about my daughter. She is a liar, a cheat and a trollop. I have had it up to here with all her antics and don't want to be responsible for her any longer. I have no idea why she is the way she is. She has been sleeping around with anything with pants on, and there is nobody she will listen to. I asked Jan Wozniak to give her a good talking to, and do you know what he told me? She made a play for him too! Imagine that? There was that Russian guard, who is gone now, thank God, and Jerzy...yes, Jerzy. Don't look so shocked Mrs. Kew. Those two want to get married!"

"What?" Vita exclaimed in disbelief.

"So now maybe you will understand my situation. You have a teenage daughter — tell me what would you do?"

"Well..." Vita recovered her composure. "Fortunately Ellie's hormones seem to be pretty dormant, and we do get along rather well, but I can see your predicament. Maybe you have been too strict with her. Maybe she does these things to rebel or to provoke you or just to spite you. I will have a talk with her. She may listen to me."

"Good luck!" Greta Karowska interrupted with a wave of her hand. "But I am afraid you will be wasting your time!"

17

THE WAR COMES HOME

June 21, 1941.
Germany invaded the USSR. Operation Barbarossa.
Italy, Rumania, Finland, Albania and Latvia declared war on Russia.

July 3.
Stalin tells his People: "A great treat hangs over our country.
We must defend it to the last."

June, 1941. Valeria Yevgenovna let Vita in and quickly closed the door behind her. Her eyes were red and swollen, her hair still not combed, and she was obviously in an agitated state.

"What is the matter?" Vita had never seen her looking this upset.

"Oh, I have been up most of the night. Igor Ivanovich just rode into Beresnik. We had a wire yesterday from his brother in Moscow. Ellie brought it. He will try to contact him by phone to get some details...."

"Valeria Yevgenovna," Vita interrupted. "What was it? What was in the wire?"

"Hitler attacked us! He declared war on Russia!"

"What? When?"

"Apparently just two days ago — the 22nd."

Vita had to sit down. Her legs felt like jelly. Her thoughts were all scrambled, confused, she couldn't make any sense out of them.

"The man is absolutely insane," she finally said. "We now have a common enemy, don't we? How will this affect the commandant and you?"

"I don't know. We will have some more information this evening when he gets back."

"Why don't you take a nap, you look all worn out. I will take care of the children's breakfast and keep them quiet," said Vita, trying very hard to keep calm. She wanted some time to herself, to absorb this bombshell, to make some sense out of it. What did it mean as far as they were concerned? She couldn't wait to get Wozniak's opinion. She cooked some oatmeal for the children and poured two small glasses of milk and called them to the kitchen. They were too small to understand any of this. Hell, she didn't understand it herself!

The housework all done, she admonished the children to be quiet, not to wake their mother and slipped out the door.

She worked fast to complete her work in the Russian workers' barracks; and when it was all done, she ran to her own house. It was only 4 p.m.; Ellie should be coming back any minute, but the others she would probably not see until later that evening. She paced up and down her little room, thinking, thinking. What if Hitler is strong enough to conquer and occupy Russia? What then? No, she immediately reasoned, this is a huge country, their military resources are immense; they will defeat him, but if they don't....

She couldn't stand it any longer. She decided to walk down the road to meet Ellie. She hurried along the wooden rail for about ten minutes when she spotted her daughter who was almost running waving her arms.

"Mother, Russia is being invaded by Germany! I just have one paper today, but I read it all!"

"I know. Valeria Yevgenovna told me."

"What will happen to us, Mother?"

"I don't know." She put her around the girl's shoulders and they walked back, deep in thought.

****

Both Wozniak and Helman sneaked into Vita's room that night. The news bowled them over. It was incredible! Wozniak sat there with a curious expression on his face.

"You know," he finally said. "this may be our salvation."

They looked at him in disbelief. What? How?

"Do you remember Napoleon Bonaparte? What happened to him when he tried to conquer Russia? Yes, I think this is the end of Hitler. Like an unsated ogre, he wants more and more, but wait till the rains come, then the winter and the snow. He will bog down first, and then he will freeze, and then Mother Russia will devour him. Mark my words!"

He left them totally confused.

"A drowning man will grasp at straws." Helman wasn't as optimistic. He was full of fear and apprehension when he finally said goodnight.

****

July, 1941. "We will be leaving within a month."

Vita stopped what she was doing and wondered whether she heard her right.

"What did you say?" she asked.

Valeria Yevgenovna took her hand into hers and repeated the sentence. Vita just stared at her. The carefully planned and engineered stick structure she put together piece by piece had just crumbled.

"Igor Ivanovich has been called to join his army unit. He has a month to wind up his affairs here and break in his replacement. The children and I will be going back to Moscow."

Vita looked at her with despair in her eyes.

"I suppose that's good news, and I am very happy for you, but it will break my heart to see you leave. You have been a good friend, and I will never forget you!"

"Vita Alexandrovna, these are terrible times for all of us. I wish we had met under different circumstances. My husband, under his gruff exterior, is a very kind and good man. I am sure he will do everything he can to see that his successor is decent and fair. I will leave you everything I can spare. I am sure there will be quite a bit of food staples and other supplies I won't be taking along."

"Thank you very much, Valeria Yevgenovna."

"Oh, and I will write. Also, if I can I will send you a package, care of Vanya. I know you are not allowed to receive any mail, but he is. I will instruct him to turn it over to you."

Vita left her with a heavy heart.

The news hit the group hard. They met in Vita's room that night, speculating, wondering and commiserating. Ellie passed around pages of "Pravda" she had been able to liberate from the post office. Reading between the lines, the war with Germany was not going well. General mobilization of the Russian Army was in effect, calling every able-bodied man. Casualties were heavy. Three hundred thousand Russians were taken prisoner by the Germans west of Minsk, and the latest and most grave news — the Germans had taken Kiev. Mrs. Kucharska was in tears.

"They will take the whole country and kill us all," she wailed.

"What about feeding us? How will we get supplies up here?" Helman wanted to know.

But Jan Wozniak just sat there with a knowing smile on his face. "Mark my words." He shook his finger at them. "They will suck the S.O.B. deep into the bowels of the country along the entire wide front and then when winter comes — goodbye Hitler! Mark my words," he repeated, rubbing his hands and chuckling quietly.

They all exchanged glances, wondering if he had lost his mind. Then they all looked at Ellie.

"What?" she asked.

"You have the only outside contact." They were all talking at once. "You have got to see if there is a way to buy or barter for food from the local people. As soon as the rains come, we will be cut off from Beresnik. Besides, who will give a damn about prisoners in labor camps when they have armies to feed? We will all starve!"

Vita came to her aid. "Now wait a minute. She is just a child. What can she do?"

"Come to think of it," Ellie just remembered something. "The post-master's wife was telling the people at the table that they expected a very good crop of potatoes this fall and they would like to sell some."

"See? That's great, Ellie. Try and find out how much they can spare and what they want for it, will you?" Ellie nodded, wondering what she was getting into.

Finally they were gone, sneaking out one by one, quietly and undetected. By the time Vita brought out her diary and lit the oil lamp, Ellie was asleep. She sat there for a long time filling the small scrap of paper with all the day's events. She mulled them over time and again. All the fears and apprehensions surfaced anew. She dreaded the change of the camp's command. Who will replace Igor Ivanovitch? Will their new work assignments continue or will they go back to hard labor? But most of all, she deplored the loss of her friend Valeria Yevgenovna. She would miss her terribly. Then she thought of Jan Wozniak and his strange behavior and predictions. Could he be right? Could Germany overextend itself and be defeated? But if not, what would happen if Hitler won? It was all incomprehensible!

****

The new commandant was a short, stocky man in his forties. He was a retired army captain. He came alone with just a few possessions. The most incredible thing, carefully carried into his quarters, was a huge Victrola and stacks of records! If it weren't for the bad limp and the permanent scowl on his face, he would just be another gray, dull-looking Russian like all the others.

Igor Ivanovitch shipped his family out in the beginning of August. Vita waved a sad goodbye to Valeria and the children. She collected the remnants of their food supplies, some winter clothing, and the old sewing machine Valeria did not want anymore.

At the next camp meeting the commandant introduced his successor: Boris Fyedorovitch Sokol. Just observing the man, the group decided that life would not get any easier under his command. After his brief speech, they were convinced of it. Efforts would have to be doubled, he told them. The Soviet Union was at war. It was in their mutual interest to work hard, to supply as much lumber as they possibly could. He pounded the table with his fist.

"We need utmost effort out of each and every man and woman. I will personally see to it that we get it!"

****

They named him "Boris, the Terrible" and cautioned each other to be very careful. No meetings for awhile. No bartering with the Russians. No complaints to Vanya.

"The less attention we draw to our group the better," admonished Wozniak. "And, Ellie, if you still have your job, be careful with the newspapers. Read them there and pass on the information, but don't take any for awhile. Let's just be very careful and not make any waves."

Vita went at her regular time to the commandant's house. Full of apprehension and fear, she knocked on the door.

"Come in." To her relief it was Igor Ivanovitch. He was packing up some of his papers and books.

"Boris Fyedorovitch, this is your housekeeper. Her name is Vita and she has been working for us for some time."

"That's fine," snapped Boris, the Terrible. "I want my office and quarters cleaned, but don't touch the record player. Keep the samovar going and stay out of my way. What does she do the rest of the day?" He turned to Igor Ivanovitch.

"She cleans the stachanoviets' bunk houses. Her daughter is the mail runner. They are both good workers and very trustworthy."

****

The new commandant was a well-organized, methodical man. His desk was bare save for the few essential items. All his papers were kept under lock and key. His two other rooms were as Spartan and neat as his office. He worked during the day writing his reports, doing rounds of the barracks with Vanya in tow, making trips to Beresnik, but each evening he cranked up his Victrola and listened to music late into the night, drinking vodka. Vita could see the empty bottles during her morning chores. He never seemed to show any effects from the enormous amounts of liquor he consumed every night. He never spoke to her. She made him a pot of tea which he drank in the kitchen while she tidied up his office. Then they switched areas. He would close the office door behind him, and she would not see him again until the next day. There was something about the man that made her uneasy and fearful. Just don't cross him, she told herself, do what you're supposed to do and get out!

The days he was gone she could relax. She always went home with a pinch of real tea and two small chunks of sugar. At night, she and Ellie would share it, drinking to Boris, the Terrible's early demise!

****

Fall, 1941. The rainy season was in full force now. It seemed like the skies had opened up and it poured day after day, night after night. For three successive days Ellie made the trip to the village and came back soaked and chilled to the bone but empty-handed. No mail, no newspapers. The only thing she carried back was the usual loaf of bread and a bag of apples for the commandant. The postmaster's wife smiled at Ellie.

"Here, child, these are for you. From the look on your face I can guess you didn't eat an apple for some time, ey?"

"You are right. I haven't even seen one! Thank you very much."

She put the two apples in her pocket and hurried home.

Boris Fyedorovitch did not come back from Beresnik that night. Vanya was in charge in his absence. He questioned Ellie whether or not she had seen him in the village. She shook her head.

"No Vanya, I did not see him or the truck. There was again no mail today. The postmaster wired Beresnik about it, but he sent me away before the answer came. Maybe the commandant has a wife or family there and is planning to stay overnight."

"He had nobody," Vanya answered. "Besides, this was an official trip. He should have been back by now."

Ellie repeated all this to her mother.

"I bet," Vita ventured, "he just got so drunk he couldn't move!"

The group got together that night without fear of being discovered. They all crowded into Wozniak's room, talking freely and speculating as to the commandant's whereabouts.

He returned the next morning while Vita was cleaning his office. Vanya carried in two crates full of bottles and a stack of papers. Boris Fyedorovitch was preoccupied and gruff.

"That's all for today," he told Vita. "You can go."

She lingered in the hallway listening at the door. In an agitated voice he was telling Vanya something about the war, the Germans, about Moscow and Kiev. She could not hear well enough to understand what he was saying, but the news must not have been good.

The next day Ellie brought a paper. There was too much in it for her to memorize. She decided to take a chance and liberate one "Pravda." The grim news was all there. Hitler had driven his forces into Russia along a wide front, pushing east as far as Moscow, Leningrad, Smolensk and Kiev. On October 19, 1941 in an unprecedented nationally broadcast speech, Stalin had proclaimed a "grave situation" for the entire country and had ordered his armies to fight to the last.

Panic spread through the group. What if Russia collapses? What are the British and the rest of western Europe doing? And how about America?

"Roosevelt and Churchill are talking at an Atlantic Conference," Wozniak read out loud.

"Talking? While the whole world is falling apart? We might as well give up; this is the end of us!" Helman was always first to fold.

"Let's pray for a very cold winter," Wozniak said quietly, folding the paper and bidding them goodnight.

****

18

THE SECOND WINTER

"Yes, I think this is the end of Hitler!
Like an unsated ogre he wants more and more,
but wait till the rains come, then the snow and the cold winter.
He will bog down first, then he will freeze and then
Mother Russia will devour him. Mark my words!"

Jan Wozniak

There was visible unrest and edginess among the Russian stachanoviets, the Commandant's aides and the work supervisors. Their hearts were not in their work. They gathered in groups and talked to each other out of earshot of the prisoners. They performed their tasks automatically, preoccupied and seemingly worried. Wozniak cornered his bartering man and listening to him, sensed the apprehension and concern. Russia was indeed in a grave situation not being able to stop the advancing Germans, giving up city after city, retreating, regrouping and trying to mount a counter-offensive with little success.

And the rains kept coming. Unseasonably warm weather continued through October when normally there should have been a considerable amount of snow on the ground. Vita checked over her food supplies. With the staples from Valeria Yevgenovna, her crock of pickled mushrooms, plus a whole sack of dried mushrooms and jars of the sugarless jam she had been preparing all through the summer and fall, she hoped to be able to survive when regular food supplies were short. Ellie had her mid-day meal most of the time at the postmaster's and she was beginning to look a little better, a little stronger. She managed to buy two large sacks of potatoes with the rubbles collected from the group and the postmaster arranged for their delivery by one of the truck drivers. They counted them out, so many per person, handling them carefully like some treasured, valuable things!

She managed to smuggle a paper once in a while for the whole group to share. Wozniak read it word for word, carefully scanning the pages, looking for some little item, some little word that would tell him his hopes and predictions were right, that somewhere, somehow, Hitler would be stopped. And then he saw it! In the middle of the second page! In big fat letters!

"DOZENS OF HEAVY GERMAN SUPPLY TRUCKS FULL OF AMMUNITION AND GEAR BOGGED DOWN IN MUDDY ROADS, WERE CAPTURED BY THE SOVIET ARMY, WHILE THE GERMANS RETREATED BEHIND THEIR LINES."

He ran first to Helman's room then to Vita's, waving the paper madly.

"What did I tell you? Look at this! It is starting to happen! This is it!" They had a hard time calming him down.

"It is just one isolated incident. Don't build your hopes up too much." Helman patted his shoulder.

"Oh, you are just mister doom-and-gloom, aren't you? The incurable fatalist. But you are wrong! It may take some time, but it is inevitable. Hitler will never conquer Russia!"

They finally retired to their own thoughts and speculations. Could he be right? Could it be possible?

****

The little old sewing machine Vita got from Valeria Yevgenovna proved to be a godsend. She mended the whole group's clothing, sewing up tears and altering some larger-sized clothes for the smaller children. From the remnants, she cut out and sewed mittens and caps. Everyone was short of underwear. It just wasn't available anywhere. She suspected that the Russians didn't wear any, except for long johns in the winter, and those were also very hard to get. Ellie bartered for some fabric with the postmaster's wife, giving her a couple of pieces of costume jewelry, and Vita sewed several briefs out of it. She had no elastic, so they were fastened with two buttons at the sides. It was better than nothing. Even buttons, thread and needles were at a premium. They couldn't buy them at the stores in Beresnik — the postmaster's wife told Ellie. If they were lucky enough to have a relative in Moscow or in one of the other large cities, and if that relative had a government job, they could sometimes send them out. Otherwise, they just made do without them. It was incredible how those people lived without any of the everyday necessities that others took for granted. Standing in line for hours for a bar of soap and being turned away without any, was an acceptable way of life that nobody really questioned nor dared to complain about. The younger generation didn't know any better, and the older people were forced into submission under the new communist rule. Some of them were eager to talk to the internees, but always looked over their shoulders, always wary of reprisals. "Father Stalin" had a firm grip on the entire nation and ruled with an iron fist. Even in Siberia, his NKVD network was everywhere. All transgressions, regardless of size and importance, were dealt with in a ruthless fashion without regard for human rights or liberties. This was an oppressed country! Would it last forever, the prisoners wondered? Would such a system be able to control this vast population? How long would it take the people to realize that communism may be ideal in the textbooks, but in reality it wouldn't work? Vita's group hashed this over and over during their late night gatherings. Jan Wozniak firmly believed that Russia was ripe for another revolution — the others disagreed. It was too late, they felt. The two younger generations were in power and the present life was all they had ever known.

****

Anya spent very little time in her new quarters. After her regular work day in the woods, she joined the other women for a sauna and then she was gone. Vita assumed that mother and daughter had been ironing things out, spending more time together. Late at night she would come to the window and tap gently on the glass pane. Ellie would get up and let her in. In the morning she was up very early and quietly left the room without waking the others.

"That's quite an invisible roommate we have here," Vita said to Ellie. "What is she doing? Is she planning to go back to her mother?"

"No, I don't think so. She has many problems she is trying to work out." Ellie was noncommittal.

"Is it true she and Jerzy want to get married?"

"I really don't know, but if they do, is it so wrong? They are both almost 18 and they love each other, so why not? Anya has had a miserable life at home; her mother is a witch. Do you blame her for wanting to get away from her? For wanting to be with somebody who is nice to her?"

Vita looked at her daughter in amazement.

"Do you mean you approve of this? Do you think this is the right time and place to be getting married and perhaps starting a family? Here? Now?"

"Mother, I am not judging her and I don't think you should either. She is my friend and if that is what she wants, then it's fine with me. I spoke to Dr. Helman about it and he will try to convince Mrs. Karowska to give them her blessing."

"That'll be the day!" Vita gave up. After all, Ellie was probably right. Anya was practically living with the boy now, so why not?

Bernie Helman kept his promise. He approached Greta Karowska during their lunch break while they were both warming their hands by the fire. He felt safer out in the open within earshot of the other workers.

"Mrs. Karowska, I want to speak to you in behalf of your daughter...."

"What? Is she pregnant again?" Greta hissed.

"No, nothing like that, but she and Jerzy want to get married and they would like your blessing. Can you do that? Can you show them...."

"You are obviously demented, my dear man. Give my blessing! Really, I can't believe you would even approach me. And who, pray tell, would marry them, a rabbi?"

"Why not?" Helman was getting angry. "Do you know anybody else who is better qualified?"

"Over my dead body!" She turned and walked away from him.

Anya was observing them from behind some trees. She knew the conversation did not go well.

Well, that's that, she said to herself. I tried. We will do it all by ourselves.

The rabbi Helman approached had to be convinced that it was all right for him to marry two Catholics. He was not quite sure he wanted to be a party to this, but it was probably better than letting the two live together without the benefit of some kind of sacrament.

They arranged to have it on a Saturday with only Jerzy's sister Nella and Helman as witnesses. It took several minutes and the young couple was pronounced man and wife. They moved Marian Kucharski into his parents' room and took up housekeeping in Jerzy's quarters. With a minimum of fuss they settled down to married life. Anya's mother was not even aware the marriage had taken place and her only daughter was now lost to her, maybe forever.

****

The winter was slow in coming but when it finally arrived, the heavy snow fell in such profusion it was hip deep and almost impassable. Work in the woods was halted for a couple of days while the prisoners dug themselves out, making tunnel-like paths from the barracks to the kitchen and meeting hall, to the latrines and bath houses. The roofs creaked under the heavy load of snow and it was necessary to rake them off for fear of the long spans collapsing. Ellie made her first trip to the village after the truck scraped some of the snow off the wooden rails. It was hard to walk in the knee-deep snow and it took her much longer to reach the village. The river had frozen over some time ago and the mail was now being delivered by horse and sleigh. Someone had already walked across that day leaving footprints for her to follow. She plowed through the path, reaching the post office exhausted and covered with snow. The noon meal was already being eaten by the regular group of people the postmaster's wife fed daily. Ellie brushed the snow from her clothes and took off her valanki to put them on top of the piechka next to a row of the others' to dry. The postmaster motioned her to sit. There was an animated conversation among the diners. The news was better. The Germans were being halted here and there. Their machinery frozen up, unable to start. The troops suffering from frostbite and lack of food. But most astounding was the news about Japan attacking the United States.

"Imagine that!" the postmaster was saying. "Now the whole world is involved."

"Will the Japs fight us too?" somebody wanted to know.

Ellie was all ears. What did it all mean? She was not sure whether this new development was good or bad. She could not comprehend any of this. Mr. Wozniak would know, she was sure. Somehow she had to get a newspaper to him.

"Hey, wake up, boy" the postmaster was saying. "There are supplies for the camp going back today. You can hop a ride."

"Oh, that's great. It's so hard to walk in this deep snow."

"The mail is all sorted. Go pick it up."

She thanked him and his wife for the meal and put on her valanki. They were nice and warm. The mail was tied with a piece of string with only one Pravda for the Commandant. No other papers were to be seen anywhere, as she frantically looked around. The truck was all loaded and ready to go. She filled her satchel and walked over to the driver.

"Can I ride back with you, please?"

"Sure." He motioned her in. A strong odor of vodka filled the small cab.

They rode in silence for a while, the tire chains biting into the snow and rolling down the two wooden rails. I have got to read that paper, Ellie thought.

"Have you read the Pravda today?" she asked the driver.

"Nah, I am not too good at that."

"Want me to read some of the news to you? There might be something interesting there."

"O.K. — if you want to."

She opened the paper and scanned the front page headlines.

JAPAN BOMBS PEARL HARBOR — SCORES OF AMERICAN
SHIPS DESTROYED — SURPRISE ATTACK STUNS THE WORLD!

She kept reading out loud trying very hard to memorize as much of it as she could. She did not think the driver was even listening to her, his attention riveted to the snow covered rails barely visible through the steamed-up windshield. He had to keep all four wheels in the ruts. If one of them slipped over the side log, the truck would be done for, marooned there for days, until a huge rescue tractor with a winch came along to right the derailed vehicle. They stopped once to stoke the two furnaces and in no time pulled into the camp. Ellie delivered the mail and the paper to Vanya and ran home.

Wozniak slipped into their room after dark.

"Did you get a paper today?" he asked.

"No, the mail was already sorted when I arrived and there was only one paper for the Commandant, but I read something there that I think is very important. It said that Japan bombed some harbor and destroyed many American warships; it was a surprise attack...."

"What harbor, Ellie?"

"I don't remember. I have never heard of it, but there were huge headlines on the front page saying that America was now involved in the war and that Germany and Italy had declared war on America also. What does it all mean?"

"I can't imagine!" He sat there scowling at her, trying to sort things out.

"How will all this affect us?" Vita asked.

"I wish I knew. The most puzzling thing to me is the fact that the Allies and Russia are fighting a common enemy — Germany. Why are we still here? Held prisoners by our own ally? Does that make any sense?
And now Japan getting into it? It's enough to drive one crazy! Please, Ellie, if you can, try to liberate another paper."

He lifted himself up from his bench and, patting Ellie on the head, let himself out of the room.

****

"Boris the Terrible" was, among other things, very unpredictable.
Some nights he and Vanya toured the camp, checking every barrack, looking for any transgression, any insubordination of the smallest kind. Then, days would pass without any activity at all. He would lock himself in and spend long nights playing his music and drinking vodka.

The night he chose to make his inspection was the night Wozniak, armed with a fresh Pravda, sneaked into Helman's room. Stan Kurcharski and Jerzy were already there. The Helman children, down with a cold, were staying at Mrs. Kos's. They hungrily read the paper, discussed all the news and agonized over their situation. There was a pounding on the door. The men froze.

"Open up!" Boris the Terrible shouted.

Wozniak frantically gestured to the others: Paper! Into the fire! Now! Jerzy opened the pieczka door and stuffed the Pravda into the brightly burning fire shutting the door tightly. Helman walked to the door and slowly cracked it open. Boris Fyedorovitch and Vanya pushed their way in.

"You are all under arrest!"

"What for?" Wozniak asked. "We were consulting the doctor here...."

"Shut up! You are charged with subversive activity against the Soviet Union."

"But Tovarish Commandant, how can that be? We are now on the same side. We have the same enemy!"

"Vanya, take them away!"

Vanya, with his ever-present rifle, ordered the men, somewhat sheepishly, to walk out in front of him. The men put their coats and hats on and, complaining loudly, filed out into the hallway. Several doors opened up. Mrs. Kucharska, Marian and Vita were out there, stunned and frightened.

"What happened? What is going on? Where are you taking them?"

"Get back to your rooms!"

In the commotion Wozniak spoke to Vita in French. "Don't worry — we burned it."

She latched her door and sat on Ellie's cot.

"They have arrested four of them!"

Ellie sat straight up. "The paper," she whispered.

"It's all right — Mr. Wozniak told me they burned it."

"What will they do to them?"

****

December 10, 1941. The four men were locked in the local brig for the rest of the night and transported the next day to Beresnik for interrogation. Marian Kucharski was the only male left in the group. He consoled his mother the best he could, but was too timid to make any inquiries of the authorities as to the fate of his father. Maria Wozniak was suffering from a bad case of scurvy as was her younger daughter Elzunia. Avitaminosis, Dr. Helman called it, lack of proper nourishment, vitamins and minerals. She had barely enough strength to get up from her cot to take care of her children. She wept in desperation, bitter and resentful. She felt abandoned by her husband, blaming him for risking his life disobeying orders. Vita, not very secure in her new job, and Ellie, afraid to be discovered for her part in the "crime," kept quiet, doing their best to stay out of the official's sight, but both feeling guilty for their cowardice. The only one with enough gumption to register a protest and inquire about the men was Anya. She wanted to know where her young husband was and what was he charged with. When was he coming back?

At the next meeting "Boris the Terrible" announced that the four men were now in a Beresnik jail sentenced to 60 days solitary confinement for flagrantly disobeying the camp's rules and conspiring to escape. There were tears and protests from the women, but to no avail. Vita took it upon herself to look after the group, to supplement their meager diet, using her ingenuity and craft. She was able to steal very small portions of food scraps from the Russian workers: a carrot, a parsnip, an onion, tiny bits of salt pork or a handful of dry beans or peas. The Russians brought these supplies from the village and had the cook prepare additional meals for them to supplement their rations.

She found that mixing these ingredients into a soup she cooked out of their regular portions of kasha, produced the most filling and satisfying meal. Some days when she had an onion, she would gather the oil off the top of their kasha portions and sauté the chopped onion in it until it was brown, and adding a spoonful of flour she would make a roux of sorts to thicken the soup and give it flavor. She and Ellie distributed it to all the others. Helman's children were with Mrs. Kos and the two little orphans, but Vita made sure they were clean and never hungry. She kept up her end of their pact.

They all missed the men terribly. Particularly the doctor. Every so often some man or woman came over from the other barracks looking for him. Injuries, frostbite and diseases went untreated. Morale sank to a new depth. Ellie kept a count of the days scratching small marks on a log above her bed.

At night they could hear the Commandant's music flowing from the office building, Tchaikovsky, Griegg, Rachmaninoff...and in the morning Vita discarded the empty bottles.

****

Another year was coming to an end. Christmas was gone without the usual gathering and celebration and Ellie carved her 18th mark on the log.

The cold was almost unbearable. The workers in the woods had bonfires to warm themselves from time to time, but Ellie's lonely walk to and from the village was becoming more than she could endure. Every morning she wished she were back in the woods with the others, but then the vision of the good hot meal and white bread and the contact with the village people would win over and she would get up and carefully wrap her feet in layers of newspapers, slipping them into her warm valanki. She put on layers of clothing under her fufaika and cinched the jacket with a belt. She put her tufted hat on, tying the ear flaps under her chin and covered it with her mother's large square wool scarf, tying it the way the postmaster's wife had shown her. It covered her forehead down to her brows and criss-crossed over her face to be tied at the back of her neck. The only visible part of her face were her eyes. Three layers of gloves and mittens completed her "costume." Swinging the satchel over her shoulder, she was now ready to walk to the office and pick up the Commandant's mail from Vanya.

With the sun shining in her face, the morning walk was not as bad as the return trip in the afternoon. It was dreadful. Between the setting sun and the falling temperatures, her warm breath under the wool scarf turned it to a stiff frozen shield. Layers of hoarfrost covered her brows and eyes, freezing her lashes shut so she could hardly see.

The day she, in frustration, ripped the scarf away from her, she ended up with a frostbitten tip of her nose.

Some days when the rails were packed down by the truck's tires, she could walk much faster swinging her arms, flexing her ice-cold hands, but when the fresh snow fell, every step was an effort. Clumps of snow stuck to her boots, weighing them down, slowing her step. She could feel her whole body cooling dangerously. Sometimes an eerie feeling would come over her, an almost irresistible urge to just sit down on the rail and close her eyes. She envisioned herself skipping through a green field full of flowers, wearing a light flowing gown, her feet barely touching the ground. And then she would hear the wolves howl and come back to reality in a split second, quickening her step to a half run. Her mother would sometimes walk out a distance from the camp to meet her, and what a welcome sight that was!

****

With the men gone, another chore fell on the remaining members of the group. The firewood. They did not realize how much of it was needed to keep the piechkas going in all the rooms. Normally, Stan Kucharski, Jan Wozniak and Jerzy saw to it, stacking the wood high in a long line just behind the building. But they were gone now so, on their days off, Ellie, Anya and Marian took over. There was a winter's supply of logs, but they had to be split into small, short chunks to fit the stoves. Anya and Ellie worked side by side. They became quite proficient, wielding the large, sharp axe. The logs, when nice and smooth without any knots, split easily with each swing, giving the girls a strange feeling of release from all their frustrations.

"Look, Ellie, Stalin's head!" Anya would hiss, placing a short stubby log on her chopping surface, and with one vicious swing splitting it in half.

"Yes, and here's Boris the Terrible," Ellie mimicked, swinging her axe.

The younger children were corralled to help carry some of the wood inside and stack it in the hallway. The rest was piled outside in huge heaps, hopefully large enough to last the week.

It was a sunny and relatively warm morning. Ellie was splitting some of the chunks for kindling. She had to hold on to the narrow, long piece of wood with one hand and with a succession of fast chops reduce it to small pieces. The last chop caught a good part of her left index finger, the axe slicing through it neatly and sending the piece of flesh and nail onto the snow bank. Totally shocked and dumbfounded, she barely felt any pain as she looked from her now bleeding finger to the morsel laying there in the snow. Later, she could never understand why she did what she did. It must have been a reflex or an instinctive move, because she reached for the little piece and placed it neatly where it came from, lining the cut nail up evenly with its other half. She then placed her thumb over it and pressed hard, holding it in place. It was bleeding quite a bit and starting to throb. Then she called for her mother.

Vita and Anya came running simultaneously. Ellie was sitting in the snow bank, holding her hand high above her head.

"What happened?" Vita looked at the trickles of blood flowing down Ellie's hand and into her sleeve.

"Show me. Where is the cut? Move your thumb!"

"I can't. If I move it, my finger will fall off!"

"What? You cut your finger off?"

"Just a piece of it, but I put it back and that's what I am holding. It hurts!"

"Put it back? Ellie, you can't do that. It will never grow back," Vita was saying. "First of all we have to clean it up. Come let's go inside and I will cook some of the Atabrine and we will wash it. Then we can bandage it."

Vita now took over.

"I am not letting go of my finger! It's clean. The axe is clean and so is the snow." Ellie could be very stubborn at times and Vita knew better not to press her.

"All right! We will just wash the hand off and when it stops bleeding we will take a look. O.K.?"

They went in and Vita put a pot of water on the stove to boil.

"I will run over to Dr. Helman's room to see if he has any bandages," Anya offered.

Ellie just sat there, pale and shocked, holding her hand up above her head, thumb pressing down on the severed piece of flesh and nail.

"I wish Dr. Helman were here," she finally said, and then the tears came.

Anya came back with two rolls of bright yellow cloth strips wrapped in toweling and tied with string.

"Those are cooked and sterile," Ellie said through her tears. "He used them on wounds."

Vita ran out with the boiling atabrine solution and set the pot in the snow to cool. Ellie swished her whole hand in it, washing off the caked-on blood. She never removed her thumb from the index finger. Vita had to bandage the two fingers together to hold them in place. The whole hand was now throbbing badly.

Ellie remembered something Dr. Helman said while treating the injured prisoners.

"Anya, would you please fill a bucket with snow and bring it in?"

Vita and Anya exchanged glances.

"Sure, I'll be right back."

She had them place the bucket full of snow on the shelf and, sitting down on the floor, buried her hand in it. The relief was almost instantaneous. When the hand got too cold she removed it, but as soon as the pain came back, in went the hand.

Anya reported the injury to Vanya who came back to the barracks with the Commandant's message.

"You have two days. If you can't go back to work, he will replace you."

"Thank you, Vanya. I am sure I can manage that."

Four days passed before she finally had to make her trip. The snow fell in such heavy amounts that everything came to a standstill. Even the locals could not remember when this much snow fell in such a short period of time. By the time the people raked some of it from the roofs, the barracks were buried up to the rafters. Deep narrow tunnels led to the essential points, the rest was impassable. The Commandant stayed in Beresnik a couple of days, waiting for the trucks to clear the path. Ellie finally gathered enough courage to peek at her finger. She carefully unwrapped the bandage holding the two fingers together and, dunking them in the atabrine solution, slowly separated her thumb from the injured finger. She almost gagged looking at the swollen, disfigured tip. The edges of the cut were black and lifted up from the wound, but the center seemed to adhere well. After painstakingly cleaning it up she bandaged it again, this time without the thumb, making sure not to move the severed portion from the finger. To her great relief, there was no sign of infection. She was resigned to the fact that the severed portion could fall off, but she was going to make every effort to save it. Dr. Helman would know what to do, but he was not there. She had to do this all on her own, hoping for the best.

The men came back on February 11th. There was joy and tears among the group as they repeatedly hugged the emaciated, haggard, hollow-eyed prisoners. The men were quiet and unwilling to talk about the ordeal even to their immediate family members. Helman, with tears in his eyes, thanked Vita for her care of his children. She told him how much many of the camp's people missed him; his very presence there seemed to be so important to them.

"Were you treated badly?" she asked.

He shook his head. "One day I will tell you all about it."

Even Wozniak, always so positive, so optimistic, moved about his chores automatically without the usual spark of energy and resourcefulness. And they all looked awful! Their shaven heads, part of the prison's de-licing program, accentuated their thin, bony features and the prison pallor.

Vita frantically cooked up pots of her now-famous soup, convinced that food was essential in bringing them around. Ellie gave up the extra slice of white bread the postmaster's wife sent home with her. Marta Kucharska somehow, somewhere, bartered for a large jar of honey and several tins of "spam" which she shared with the other men. The group was never as close as they were during that hard, long winter.

****

"Do you realize we have been here almost two years? Two years!"
Vita said to Ellie, as she wrote down her latest thoughts. "Next week you will be sixteen years old! You have lost two of the best years of your life and God only knows how long this will last." She could not hold back the tears.

"Mother, please don't cry. Look at it this way." She jumped off her cot and flexed her forearm muscles. "I am a stachanoviet's lumberjack! And a mail runner! I could probably qualify for the Olympics! And I saved my finger! See, the center is pink, it is going to live!"

Vita couldn't help but smile, wiping off her tears.

"Your father will never believe this!"

Ellie gave her mother a hug. She did not want to talk about that. That was something she could not cover up with an antic or glib words. That hurt was deep and ever present.

****

Dr. Helman resumed his rounds of the camp with Ellie helping whenever she was available. She had told him about her accident and he looked the finger over carefully, shaking his head.

"Whatever made you put the piece back, Ellie?" he asked.

"I have no idea. I just did it! Mother and Anya thought I was crazy, that it would never work."

"Well, I am sure you will lose the nail, but it will grow back and the edges, where the skin sloughed off will fill in with new tissue. It's remarkable! I am very proud of you!"

****

The actual number of dead was never made known to the prisoners, but it was enormous. Vita wanted to be sure to make that information a part of her diary. She was positive that either she or Ellie would one day hand it over to some authority to be published, to be used in exposing the communist regime, letting the world know of these atrocities committed against civilian men, women and children. Helman had a vague idea, but did not keep actual count. After resuming his routine checks, he could not help but notice the half-empty bunk houses and family rooms, once filled to capacity.

Starvation, avitaminosis, beri-beri, accidents and epidemic diseases were but a few of the causes of this decimation of life. Somebody, somehow, had to be told! Boris the Terrible kept records, but they were under lock and key and Vita never stayed in his office any longer than she had to. Vanya was the only other official close to the Commandant, but he was too loyal, too young, too dedicated to approach. The other officials were assigned mostly to food and clothing supplies, work-norm records and propaganda meetings, so the dead and the dying were of no concern to them; the fewer they had to feed and clothe, the better. Then she thought of the postmaster and the villagers. Somebody there was burying the dead — they had to know. Ellie might be able to find out.

****

The men lived in constant fear of Boris the Terrible's wrath. He seemed to go out of his way to torment the prisoners, looking for the slightest sign of rule infringement or insubordination. He had a warped, sadistic mind, half-pickled by the huge quantities of vodka he consumed every night. Even Vanya seemed startled and uneasy observing his fits of temper and irrational behavior. Some mornings his office door would be locked and his bed not slept in. The days he traveled to Beresnik, the group would relax, hoping he would stay overnight. They could then get together, eager to talk, share the news and lift each other's spirits. These meetings, though, were few and far between.

"Moze go szlag trafi!" (I hope he has a fatal stroke) said Wozniak.

"Either that, or he will die of alcohol poisoning," Helman added. "Vanya came to get me the other day. He was scared; he could not wake him up. Well, the man was laying on the floor, passed out, an empty bottle next to him."

"What did you do?"

"What could I do? We covered him up and let him sleep it off. I told Vanya to report it to the authorities."

"Good for you!" Wozniak for a change approved of the doctor's move.

****

The postmaster came to the table after everybody had started to eat their lunch. He was smiling at Ellie.

"I have some good news for you. Just heard it over the radio. You might all go free quite soon!"

Ellie choked on her borscht. She gaped, wide-eyed, from face to face, not able to say anything, not able to breathe.

"What did you say?" she finally croaked.

"Well, there seems to be some organization, some group, working with our government to release all the Polish prisoners from camps. I am sure they will let you know very soon."

Ellie just sat there dumbfounded, in total shock. She didn't know what to do — cry, jump up and down, yell.

"Are you sure? Did you hear right?"

"Oh, yes, no doubt about it."

"Thank you, tovarish. If the mail is ready, I would like to leave right now."

She ran most of the way, her thoughts scrambled, her heart pounding, her breath raspy. God, I hope I don't drop dead before I get there, she thought. But when she finally reached the camp, there was nobody there to tell the news to. She paced up and down the hallway, waiting. Finally she ran out to the Russian bunkhouse looking for her mother. She spotted her, scrubbing the boards of a long harvest table. You won't have to do that anymore, Ellie thought.

Vita looked up, startled to see her there.

"What is it? Anything wrong?"

"No, Mother, hurry up, let's go home. I have something to tell you."

"But I am not finished...."

"Never mind, this is more important!"

Vita gathered her things and followed her daughter out of the barracks. Ellie was now running waving her mother on. Latching the door behind them, she said in half-whisper: "The postmaster told me it's all over! We will be free soon! We can go home!"

Vita sat down on her cot. She stared at the girl who was jumping up and down, waving her arms and crying — all at the same time.

She has lost her mind, Vita thought.

"Here, Ellie, sit down next to me and tell me, slowly, what did you hear? Where did the postmaster get it?"

"All right." She wiped her eyes and repeated the news, word for word, as she had heard it.

"I don't believe it! Are you sure? Why haven't we been told? We have got to let Mr. Wozniak know, and the others. Let's not go into any details as yet. Let's just say that there is something afoot, that there are rumors. I don't want to build their hopes up, if it's not true. You understand?"

"Yes — let's do it tonight."

They made their rounds late after supper, sneaking in and out of rooms, dropping their bombshells in whispers, imploring their friends to keep calm and quiet. The forever-pessimistic doctor reacted accordingly.

"Oh, it's not possible. It must be a mistake, somebody is playing a cruel joke on us."

Wozniak was excited. "I knew it! It had to happen! I wonder who is doing it?"

****

19

FREE TO GO!
BUT WHERE?

November 1941.
The Red Army halted the tired German Forces
with huge numbers of fresh Soviet Reserves.
For the first time in World War II the German Armies
began to retreat. Churchill declared:
"Any man or state who fights the Nazis will have our aid.

All those long years during which the prisoners felt forgotten and abandoned there was, in fact, a liaison man in Moscow, representing the Polish government in exile in London, headed by General Sikorski. This representative had been sent there to protest the mass shipments of hundreds of thousands of Poles and Jews into labor camps all over Russia following its occupation of eastern Poland. But not until Germany declared war on the Soviet Union and mounted a successful invasion into the heart of Russia was Stalin forced into an alliance with the western countries.

RELEASE THE POLES! OPEN UP THE CAMPS! was General Sikorski's demand. It took several months after Hitler's invasion to finally pressure Stalin to sign an agreement with the Sikorski government and comply with its demands for an immediate amnesty for all the Poles. Permission was given to the British to let several repatriation groups into Russia to head the massive search for and organization of all those released from the various forced-labor camps. The southern region of the Soviet Union, namely Uzbekistan, was selected as the assembly center for the fledgling Polish Army headed by General Anders.

Strange towns like Kuybishev, Narpay, Kitab, Karkin-Batash, Guzar, Kermine and JangiJul were to provide facilities and army induction centers for all the men and women who were physically able to get there and put on uniforms.

But, of course, the few hundred survivors in Camp Vozemka had no idea what was happening. The announcement from Boris the Terrible came at their next general meeting. It was short and to the point. By the order of the Soviet Soyuz, they were free — no longer prisoners! The camp would be closed within a month. Vozemka would be abandoned, as would many other neighboring camps!

Shouts of joy and jubilation drowned out the rest of his speech.
He was no longer feared. There were a few fists raised in his direction as he hastily packed up his papers and, flanked by Vanya and other officials, left the room retreating to his quarters.

"I have a good mind to knock his block off," said Stan Kucharski, clenching his fist.

His wife hung on to him, tears streaming down her face.

"Forget him, Stasiu. We are free. We don't have to be afraid of him anymore."

The group was overjoyed. Women were hugging each other, crying and laughing at the same time. The men were slapping one another on the back.

"What did I tell you, eh?" Wozniak kept repeating. "I just knew it couldn't last after we all became allies! I wish I knew who was behind this."

They slowly walked to their barracks, still unsure, still not quite believing, still not quite convinced.

Vita could not put into words all the thoughts and emotions crowding her mind. She wrote sentence after sentence without finishing any of them. It was a jumble of words, disconnected and chaotic. She finally gave up. It was late and Ellie was sound asleep. She walked over and sat on the edge of her daughter's cot, lightly stroking her hair. She could not stop the tears. The nightmare was coming to an end. I won't be bringing home a baby anymore, she thought, looking at the sleeping girl. How she had changed; how grown up she was; how mature at the tender age of sixteen.

****

The next morning Vanya came over and handed Vita four letters. They were from Valeria Yevgenovna!

"They were addressed to me," he said, "so I opened them. I didn't give them to you because it was against the rules. Now, I guess, it's okay."

Vita held the envelopes, turning them over and over. This was the first mail she had received since the outbreak of the war. She thanked him.

"What will you do now, Vanya?"

"The camp will stay open for a month, but I'll be going back to my unit much earlier, and then probably to the front, but first I have to get Boris Fyedorovich to a hospital. He is a very sick man. Where is the doctor? Do you suppose I could talk to him?"

He was a decent young man, just doing his job.

****

The whole group got together in Vita's room to talk their situation over. A large pot of soup was simmering on the stove. As always, they came armed with bowls and spoons, the men carrying benches to sit on.

There were twelve adults and fifteen opinions! Everybody had a different idea as to what to do next. Finally Jan Wozniak put an end to the commotion.

"Look, obviously we know nothing! There must be a way to find out who got us released and what we are supposed to do now. Ellie, you and I will walk over to the post office tomorrow. Bernie, why don't you try to get to Beresnik to the doctors you know."

Before Helman could open his mouth to object, Wozniak stopped him with a wave of his hand.

"Bernie, just try it! Tell Vanya you need to take one of the sick Jews to the hospital. Tell him he is dying, do something! Mrs. Kew, maybe the stachanoviets know something. I know most of them are ignorant, but they do go home to the villages, they read newspapers. We also know there are other camps not too far away. Let's find out where they are and what they are doing."

"I'll do that," Jerzy volunteered. "One of the Russian workers was transferred from another camp. He was telling us about it."

"Good! Anybody else? Can you think of anything or anybody we could tap for information? That's the most important thing — TO KNOW!"

Ellie took great joy in making the trip to the village with Jan Wozniak. Marching ahead, she turned back to the huffing, puffing man and urged him on. "Come on, come on, it's not too much further."

"You said that an hour ago. Hey, wait up. I am out of breath. I am an old man!"

She giggled and laughed and let him rest awhile.

The postmaster was glad to see her. They were both welcomed to their table at noon and after the large, good meal, walked over to the post office.

"We would really appreciate it if you could tell us all you know about this new development regarding our release. Who is behind it? What are we to do next?"

"Well, all I know is that the British and your government in London...."

"Our government is in London?" Wozniak was dumbfounded.

"Yes, headed by General Sikorski. There are many repatriation groups comprised of Poles and the British already in this country setting up centers to receive all of you and, if I understand it correctly, form an army somewhere in the southern region. All the Poles are apparently quite eager to fight the Germans. General Anders is the man to head the army part, but the civilians are also to be organized. What they will do with them, I don't know. The closest center for you to report to is Kotlas. That's where the railroad starts. You should have been told all this by the commandant. The people in Kotlas know you are here. I replied to the inquiries that were sent around by the International Red Cross telling them what I knew about Vozemka and the other camps in this area."

Wozniak sat there completely overwhelmed, trying to remember every detail, sort it all out and absorb it.

"As soon as the weather breaks, I suggest you get going. The sooner you get to Kotlas, the better," the postmaster said.

He gave Wozniak a copy of Pravda and handed a packet of mail and papers to Ellie.

"I don't have to do this anymore," she said.

"I know, but it will help me out."

Ellie smiled, taking the bundle from him. "I'll do it for you, and thank you for all the help and all the food. I would like to come over occasionally to see you, if you don't mind."

They shook hands. It was time for them to start back.

****

Vanya didn't lose any time getting Boris the Terrible out of the camp and into the hospital. Helman refused to see him or go with him. The few officials left to oversee the running of the camp busied themselves mainly with procurement and distribution of food. Most of the stachanoviets left the camp as soon as they could. The saunas, latrines and the removal of the sick and dead were left to the prisoners to deal with, since no one was in charge. Wozniak took it upon himself to try to organize some of the Jews and his own group to fire the furnaces in the bathhouses and keep the latrines disinfected and clean. He got very little cooperation. They balked at being ordered around by him, resentful and surly.

A number of men came over from two neighboring camps eager for any scrap of information, any news, any directions. They all gathered in the meeting room where Wozniak told them all he had learned. The people went absolutely crazy, debating, shouting, fighting. What to do next was a question on everybody's lips. Most of them felt that somebody, somehow would come all the way to Siberia, find the labor camps and rescue them! The idea of leaving the camps on their own and traveling to Kotlas seemed preposterous to them. They couldn't possibly make it in their poor physical condition. It was sheer madness they felt.

Wozniak kept reminding them that once the Russian officials left the camps, there would be no one to supply food or transportation of any kind. But he could not convince them. Vita's group, with the exception of Mrs. Karowska and Mrs. Kos, was of the opinion that waiting to be rescued would be foolish. They wanted to get under way immediately in spite of the snow and the uncertain March weather.

"It will be a murderous trip," Wozniak warned them. "Walking with small children and sick, weak people, it will take a long time to get to Kotlas. It's approximately three hundred kilometers."

"I can't go," wept Mrs. Kos. "I would never make it."

Some of the younger, stronger Jews were for it, others thought it insane, and many didn't care anymore. Ellie recognized the young man with the axe wound. He organized a group of his own, urging, encouraging and consulting with Helman and Wozniak. After agonizing for days, a decision was made. People physically able were to be divided into small groups with one leader. They would start making immediate preparations for the journey. All extra bread was to be dried into large hard chunks. Other food anybody could barter for was to be stored. Vita made rucksack-like pouches for each person to carry. Stan Kucharski built two sleds for the children and extra luggage. He affixed an axe and saw to each sled. He made two harnesses out of heavy rope and attached those to the sleds. Ellie and Jan Wozniak made several trips to Vozemka where they obtained a map, matches, and tobacco and tried, in vain, to bribe one of the truck drivers to take them to the next town. The trucks were government property, they were told, and no one was allowed to use them.

The most agonizing decision was to leave the two women behind. Mrs. Kos and Greta Karowska were absolutely in no condition to walk that distance. The men collected enough food for them to live on after the kitchen closed and promised to send somebody for them. There were tears of frustration and regret when the day finally came for the first small group, with Wozniak in charge, to depart. It was the end of March, 1942. The second group, headed by Helman, was to leave a week later with others to follow at similar intervals.

There was still much snow on the ground, but the days were warmer with spring just around the corner. The plan was to walk approximately twenty to twenty-five kilometers a day, then set up camp around a bonfire and rest. Wozniak estimated, at that pace, they would reach Kotlas within fifteen days. There were ten people in the first group: Jan Wozniak, his wife and two daughters, Vita and Ellie, Jerzy, his two sisters and Anya.

The first two days passed uneventfully. Nights were very cold in spite of the large bonfire and a bedding of thick layers of pine branches. Both days they were a few miles short of their original goal. The village people they encountered were leery and suspicious of the rag-tag band. It was difficult to barter for food. They questioned Wozniak repeatedly, treating him like a fugitive.

"You know, these people only know how to respond to orders," Wozniak said to Vita. "They are so conditioned by the government, they are afraid to do anything on their own. They don't trust us; they don't believe us."

Vita thought that over. "Well, if they want or need an order, then why not give them one?"

"What do you mean?"

"Listen, how hard would it be for you to write up a few official sounding sentences, ordering them to help us?"

"Mrs. Kew, I could kiss you! Of course! We really have nothing to lose and this might save us!"

Vita dug one of the last trinkets out of her purse. "We'll need paper and ink," she said. She smoothed her hair down, put on a tiny dab of lipstick and looked herself over in her purse mirror. "I am ready."

They had just passed a general store of sorts somewhere down the street. They retraced their steps and Vita walked in. There were just a few items on the shelves.

"Yes?" the clerk asked.

She put on one of her bright smiles and in her best Russian asked him if she could buy some writing paper and ink. He did not have any at the store, but he could get some if.... She understood him very well.

"Oh, comrade, I have a nice gold chain here, or earrings...."

He looked at the items with interest. He disappeared behind a partition and, after a few agonizing minutes, came back with a handful of writing paper and a small bottle of ink. "You need a pen too?"

"No, thank you. I have one."

She handed him the chain and the earrings in exchange for a nice stack of paper and ink. She ran out of the store and joined Wozniak who was anxiously waiting for her at the corner.

"I've got it! Let's find a place where you can write!"

"How about the post office? I have an idea what I will say."

The group waited for him at the edge of a small park. Ellie was leery of the whole idea, but there was no arguing with the two. Maria Wozniak wiped off a few tears.

"He will never learn; always taking chances; always putting us in danger. What will we do if they arrest him again?"

"We have no alternative," Vita spoke up. "We will never make it to Kotlas at this rate. This is our only hope. We have got to get help from the villagers. I am out of things to barter with and they don't want any money. You have got to trust us!"

The page of paper Wozniak produced had quite a few lines of script-like writing and was signed at the bottom. It looked good and official.

"Whose name did you use?" asked Vita.

"Boris Fyedorovich Sokol!"

"Oh, God, do you think that's a good idea?"

"Why not? They don't know him and I think it sounds good!"

Vita looked the page over again. "It's too clear, too readable. I wish we had some kind of stamp or seal to put on it."

"Do you suppose we could make one? But out of what?" asked Wozniak.

"We could carve it out of a potato," Ellie popped up. "Smear it with ink and press it partially over the signature."

They looked at each other in total amazement. Jerzy had already opened up his pocketknife and handed it to Ellie.

"Here, let me draw it on a piece of paper," Anya volunteered. "What do you want on it? Hammer and sickle?"

"Yes, yes! Can you do it?"

The girl proved to be quite an artist. She made several drawings of very believable official-looking seals.

"Too complicated," said Ellie. "We can't carve all this in a potato."

"Okay. Let's make it simple," Anya obliged.

They finally decided on one with a hammer and sickle in the center, surrounded by a plain, thick line with a couple of leaves framing the bottom of the seal. It was beautiful!

The carving was much more difficult. They spoiled several potatoes, finally coming up with one, quite decent-looking carving.

Vita produced a couple of pages of paper and the ink bottle. They tried it many times before the potato soaked up enough ink to make a decent impression.

"Now, move it a little," Vita instructed. "It will look slightly smeared."

Ellie signed the name, over and over, on the trial pages and placed the seal in different positions.

"There, that's perfect!" exclaimed Wozniak.

He produced the original "document," signed it, and with a trembling hand, Ellie affixed the seal. When it was completely dry, Wozniak folded it carefully and put it in his breast pocket. He crossed his fingers and looked up toward the sky. They decided to try it out on the next unsuspecting village official they came across.

"Are you in charge of this kolhose? I am Jan Wozniak. We are on our way to Kotlas. Here are our orders."

With his heart pounding, he handed the letter to the frowning man. It said something to this effect: Comrade Jan Wozniak and his family are traveling under the orders of the N.K.V.D. Transportation, food and lodgings are to be provided for them. They will report to me personally upon their arrival in Kotlas. Please extend them every courtesy.

The man glanced at the letter and handed it back to Wozniak.

"How did you get here?" he asked.

"Oh, well, we were, ah, brought by a man from Vozemka, but his horse went lame."

"I see. How many are you?"

"Ten — that includes four small children. They are very tired and hungry."

"You can eat with us tonight. If there is enough room you can sleep in the kitchen. There are two or three sleds with grain leaving tomorrow morning. You can ride with them."

"Thank you, comrade," Wozniak said, pocketing his letter.

They shared the evening meal with the kolhose workers. Two large wooden bowls with good, hot soup and mashed potatoes with chunks of fried bacon mixed in were placed on the table together with slices of bread. Ellie knew exactly what to do.

"See, Mother, this is just like the postmaster's meals," she said, dipping into the communal bowls. They enjoyed their meal tremendously. The Russians observed them with curiosity, but asked few questions.

"You can sleep on the piechka, it's nice and warm," the kolhose chief said pointing to the long, high brick stove/oven running the full length of the kitchen wall. There were two stepladders to climb up on, one at each end. The entire surface was covered with fur rugs.

"Don't they sleep in beds?" Vita asked.

"Not in the winter," Ellie answered. "The postmaster's house had the same sleeping arrangement."

"How odd." Vita was standing on the stepladder checking the fur rugs with a jaundiced eye. "Let's use our own blankets."

Wozniak and Jerzy stretched out on the benches, and the women and children climbed up on top of the piechka and soon they were all fast asleep.

****

It was hard to comprehend how gullible and frightened most of the village officials were. The travelers were careful to pick small settlements, preferably kolhoses, where food was a little more plentiful and the people less sophisticated. On some occasions the "document" wasn't even needed. The driver explained the situation to the head of the village and another relay of transport was arranged. They arrived in Kotlas ahead of schedule.

****

20

THE GATHERING AT KOTLAS

From May to August 1942, the Nazis conquered the Crimea,
Ukraine and the Caucasus Mountains.
Finally the Soviet Army engaged the Germans
in one of the greatest battles in history.
The Battle of Stalingrad. 330,000 Germans were destroyed.
It marked a significant turning point in World War II.

If they expected some kind of haven, some kind of salvation or solution to their dilemma, they were sorely disappointed. The city of Kotlas was overrun by thousands of gaunt, sickly Poles clamoring for attention, medical help, food and housing. They came in droves from all directions. Young and old, men, women and children...all anxious, debilitated and hungry.

The authority there, comprised of British and Polish uniformed personnel, worked in 24 hour shifts, housing, feeding, clothing and classifying the refugees. The two local hospitals overflowed with makeshift beds filling each available space.

The first order of the day for Wozniak's group was to find someone in charge and report the fact that thousands of prisoners were still in Siberia, unable to travel, expecting to be transported out of the camps and united with their families. They were told there was just not enough personnel to do that. They were shorthanded everywhere. They needed doctors, nurses, nutritionists, drivers. They were overwhelmed by the numbers of people descending on them. This was supposed to be just a transit classification center with a railroad facility to transport the freed prisoners south to Tashkent, but it had certainly gotten out of hand. They promised that as soon as more crews and equipment arrived from England, small search parties would be dispatched to bring the remaining prisoners out. The International Red Cross already had groups of volunteer field workers combing some of the areas known to them to have scores of labor camps.

"But it may be too late for some of the women and children we left behind," Wozniak insisted. "It's only three hundred kilometers. With any kind of transport it should take no time at all!"

"We can't spare anybody right now. There are several vehicles on their way. We might be able to use a couple of those for that purpose," they said.

"We'll go back to get them!" Jerzy and Wozniak volunteered.

The group was housed in an old gymnasium. Army field kitchens were set up in several strategic spots. The food was mostly British army rations, plus cauldrons of greasy soup, large portions of bread and COFFEE! The coffee lines were always the longest. Vita discovered a pack of real cigarettes in each ration of food! There was powdered milk for the children, some cocoa mix and tins of corned beef. Water had to be boiled at all times, and the rich food eaten very sparingly for fear of intestinal rebellion, resulting in bad cases of dysentery.

Two weeks after the first group's arrival, Helman brought his charges in from the camp and there was a tearful and joyous reunion.

"How is my mother and Mrs. Kos?" Anya inquired.

"They are both fine," said Helman. "We left them with enough wood and food supplies to last them at least a month. The camp is officially closed. Is somebody going up to get them?"

"Jerzy and Mr. Wozniak volunteered to go as soon as a couple of lorries are available and the roads dry up a bit," Anya replied.

"Did you walk all the way here?" Ellie asked.

"No, we were lucky to get a ride in a large van for most of the distance. How about you?"

"Ask Mr. Wozniak." Ellie smiled at them.

****

There were wildly spreading rumors that because of the unexpectedly huge numbers of refugees, only men able to join the army, their families and auxiliary help were to be taken out of Russia to neighboring countries. The fate of the others was unknown. It was preposterous, if true, and every devious method was used to somehow qualify for that enviable status.

Vita immediately registered with the local hospital, claiming to be a nurse. She got a Red Cross band for her upper arm and was assigned to work at the hospital's dispensary. Ellie worked with Dr. Helman, making rounds and assisting him. All the men added their names to the lists circulated by the British, expressing willingness to join the Polish Army which was supposed to be organized in Tashkent and then shipped out to the German fronts. They falsified their ages, lied about their health conditions and disabilities. They wanted out of Russia at any cost! Not a single one of them would feel free until they were out of Soviet Russia.

The process of classifying and grouping the refugees for transport south proved to be an endless task, but finally some semblance of order was established, and train after train was loaded and dispatched south on a tortuous route, heading toward Kazakstan and eventually the city of Tashkent.

Jan Wozniak and Jerzy made the trip back to Vozemka as soon as a lorry was available and brought out Mrs. Kos and Greta Karowska along with several other women and children. They were mobbed and almost overpowered by several frantic prisoners who hung on the lorry, convinced this was their last chance to be rescued. Wozniak had to swear to them that everybody would be evacuated in due time.

****

21

THE LONG TREK OUT

"...It was also too late for the Wozniak's younger daughter Elzunia.
The once beautiful little girl was now a wizened,
skeletal form on spindly, bony legs with distended abdomen
and huge blue eyes that just stared, questioning not understanding.
She died quietly in her sleep of Beri-beri –
a strange disease nobody in the group had ever heard of..."

"Well, here we go again," said Vita climbing into a box car and looking around at the familiar sight. The car was clean and only twenty people were assigned to each, making it much more comfortable and roomy. The "shelves" were lined with clean mattresses. A pillow and two wool khaki blankets were folded on each mattress. Otherwise everything else was the same: stove, water barrel, benches and the hole behind a partition. Only the mood of the occupants was different. The future was still quite nebulous with the war raging on all fronts, but the direction was right. They were going back, one step at a time, one destination after another — OUT OF RUSSIA! That was their ultimate goal. They really did not care where...just over a border, any border, away from this oppressed, hellish country!

British army food rations were stacked in one corner and so was plenty of wood for the stove. There were just seven or eight cars leaving Kotlas, but others were to be added at a few locations down the line. They spent endless time examining Wozniak's map. It looked like a long trip, the railroad winding around strange provinces. There appeared to be just one train line going to Tashkent through the large cities of Kirov, Ishevsk, Orenburg and onto a vast thinly populated desert region called Kazakstan, around the Aral Sea, and finally to Tashkent located on the border of Uzbekistan and Kirgistan.

"Dear Lord!" exclaimed Vita. "How long will it take us? It looks like three thousand kilometers!"

"It will take a long time," agreed Wozniak. "There are two or three Polish 'chiefs' running this train with a Russian crew. They said we will make many stops to take on coal and food, wherever army kitchens are set up, and again, this being only a single line, we will sit on the sidetracks."

They settled down to a sedentary, dull life. There was nothing to do besides the daily routine tasks. Jan Wozniak, forever the professor, again organized his students for daily sessions of lessons in anything he could teach them — history, geography, mathematics, Russian grammar. They wrote little essays about their experiences in Siberia, first in Polish, then translated them into Russian. He corrected all the papers and graded them diligently. He was such an excellent, interesting teacher, the children loved their lessons. Then, to break the monotony, during their stops in larger cities, he would organize excursions. Sometimes they would go to museums, if there were any; sometimes to botanical gardens or just for walks through town peering into empty stores, visiting with the people, enjoying the sights. The weather was perfect...sunny and warm with occasional spring showers.

The train moved on at a decent pace with the predictable stops and layovers. Now and then, along the route, other cars full of refugees were added. They came from salt mines, copper and zinc mines and farm kolhoses. Their stories were more or less the same. Wozniak befriended many Catholic families; there were nuns, priests, many officials, teachers, doctors and university professors. It seemed like the entire intelligentsia of a town or city had been rounded up and shipped into Russia. They were all in a deplorable state of health, emaciated, with hollow faces and sunken eyes. Wozniak and some of the group would sit with them on the sunny platform exchanging bits of information, speculating as to their future destination and eventual return home.

The younger teenage children liked to ride on the open flat car which was added to the middle of the train. There was some kind of machinery covered with canvas tarps at one end, but most of the surface was open and great to stretch out on and sunbathe. Usually Ellie, Anya, Jerzy, Marian and Nella would hop onto the flat car after their midday meal and sunbathe until the next stop, then return to their own car. Sometimes they were joined by other children. It was great fun talking and playing games. At dusk the train would usually come to a stop for the evening meal.

Ellie looked at her watch. "Hey, it's almost six o'clock; it's getting chilly out here. Why aren't we stopping?"

Jerzy leaned out to look ahead, hoping to spot signs of some civilization, but all he could see was the same vast, uninhabited land, without any settlements, any signs of life. They huddled together with their backs to the canvas-covered machine waiting for the train to stop. It was almost dark when finally the train slowed down to a slow roll and Jerzy decided to make a run for it. He held his little sister's hand and they both jumped off. Anya followed, then Marian and Ellie. The train was rolling slower than their running speed and they caught up easily with their car. One after another got on with the help of Stan Kucharski who pulled them up with ease.

Ellie tripped in some gravel just as she reached for the outstretched hand and fell to her knees. By the time she got up her car passed her by. Stan Kucharski watched her anxiously as she kept running alongside the train and finally saw her grab the handrail of the caboose and hop on the steps. She waved to him to let him know she was all right. The steps led to a small compartment with benches and a sleepingbunk. There was a high desk with a stool next to it and some remnants of food were strewn about the surface. There was a cap and a jacket hanging on a hook. She yelled out a greeting. A door opened up and a Russian train crewman came out of what looked like a washroom. He staggered out hanging on to the walls of the caboose. He was just as surprised to see her there as she was to see him. She tried to explain what had happened, but he wasn't listening. He kept coming closer. Fumes of alcohol breath enveloped her.

"Ay, kreasnaya dievushka," he finally said, reaching for her. She pushed his arm away, took a couple of steps backwards and was forced to sit down on the bench. He kept coming at her, grabbing her shoulder and grinning a horrible snaggle-toothed grin. She shouted at him to leave her alone, but he kept grabbing her arms.

In desperation she bent both her legs up and with all the strength she could muster, kicked him in the groin. He let go of the wall and, doubling over in pain, fell backwards, out the open door, down the steps, onto the gravel path and then rolled down the grassy embankment, yelling and cursing as he disappeared from view. Ellie held her breath. With her heart pounding wildly she stood in the doorway holding on to the handrails, leaning out to see where the man was, afraid he might catch up with the slow-moving train. But there was no sign of him. She looked the other way. Somebody was leaning out her own car waving to her. She waved back. She was okay.

The train finally stopped at 9 p.m., and she ran over to get an earful of words from her mother and all the others.

"Don't you ever do that again!" Vita was almost in tears.

Ellie sat quietly on her bed saying nothing. All she could think of was the horrid, drunken man falling down the steps. Was he alive? Was he hurt? Should she report it? What would happen to her if she did? Or if she didn't? She agonized over it all night long, not able to erase the picture of that ugly, contorted face and the frantically flaying arms trying to catch the caboose railing. By the morning train-stop, she made her decision.

"Mr. Wozniak, can I speak with you...alone?"

He walked with her behind the field kitchen. "What is it, Ellie?"

She told him the whole story, barely able to hold back the tears.

"Well, you did the right thing, sweetheart." Wozniak put his arm around her. "You had no choice!"

"I didn't know he would fall off the train. What if he got killed or badly injured?"

"You can't worry about that. I will report it to the train officials; we shall see what they think."

"Will you do that? I would be very grateful."

"Certainly, my dear. Don't worry about it. He was probably so drunk he wasn't even hurt."

The incident was never mentioned again. Wozniak told the Polish official who dismissed it with a shrug. Ellie never told her mother or anyone else, but that drunken, horrified face of the falling man haunted her for years. She never again joined the others on the flat car; she was afraid to be seen by any of the train crew; she lived in fear of one day coming face to face with that man. It was like a nightmare.

****

Two weeks into the journey the landscape had changed so drastically that the travelers would keep the car doors wide open to observe with wonder the barren, desert-like land. The people inhabiting those plains were yellow-skinned and slightly slant-eyed. They lived in mud huts, tended herds of goats and rode fast, wild horses. They waved to the passing train and whenever there was a layover, they came in small groups offering their goat cheese and kefir. They spoke a language no one understood, but smiled happily, pocketing the money the train people offered them.

Wozniak made small notations on his map whenever they stopped or passed a town or a province. The train stayed two full days in Ksyl-Orda, a sizeable Kazakstan city, where they were able to make excursions and mingle with the aborigines. They were friendly, but shy and forever watchful not to be seen in long conversations with the foreigners. Ksyl-Orda had a magnificent Russian Orthodox Church with several gold cupolas on high spires. The church was closed and services forbidden, but the older Russians pointed to it with pride remembering the old, better times.

There were approximately 500 kilometers still to be covered and although the train moved at a good pace, much time was lost in layovers and food and coal stops. Finally, after days of anticipation, the train rolled into Tashkent, a large bustling city with an airport, hotels, government buildings, beautiful parks and a large population. The final destination was JangiJul, south of Tashkent, where the entire area had been turned over to the British/Polish command for the organization and formulation of several divisions under General Anders.

A sea of army tents covered the sandy plains with little vegetation and practically no trees. The temperatures hovered around one hundred degrees and the only relief came at night when they dropped drastically, down to fifty or sixty degrees.

The group was assigned to several tents and very quickly became organized and settled. The process of re-registering and classifying the men and women was faster and much more efficient. New, clean British uniforms including shoes and assorted gear were issued to all the men. Ellie signed up with the A.T.S. (British Auxiliary Transport Service) and had a picture taken in her new uniform. After an interview with a high-ranking woman officer, she was assigned as a courier driving a jeep between the different posts, delivering orders, reports and supplies.

Vita was kept busy altering the uniforms that were issued to the group. The smallest sizes available were too big to fit the emaciated bodies. Ellie weighed 79 pounds and her uniform skirt slid off her hips down to her ankles. Her shirt collar could accommodate another neck. She modeled the clothes in front of the laughing children, turning this way and that, striking funny poses.

The uniforms, with the exception of the poplin shirts, were all wool and very hot. The cotton issue had not as yet arrived from England, but all the uniformed "soldiers" were ordered to wear ties, jackets and caps. Ellie raced her jeep down the desert roads, cooling off in the breeze. Her felt-covered canteen, soaked in water and hung outside the car door, cooled down the contents of good, sweet coffee Vita had fixed for her.

Other treats were the watermelons. Somebody devised a method for cooling them. They were lowered into a well in a net-like harness. After leaving them overnight, the fruit was cool and refreshing and safe to eat. Most of the water, however, was contaminated. There was no defense against a variety of diseases that plagued a large number of the refugees.

The men and women inducted into the army were housed in separate tents, their families clustered close by. Vita and Ellie were separated. Vita lived with the nurses and hospital staff; Ellie shared a tent with other A.T.S. young women. They were able to visit each other as the tents were close to one another and an ample amount of free time was allowed for rest, due to their debilitated physical condition. At the field hospital there were two three-hour shifts — one in the morning and the other in the afternoon, evening or night.

Vita, Ellie and Anya spent most of their free time together as Jerzy was training in another camp several kilometers away. He would come back every second weekend to see his wife and sisters. He looked very handsome in his uniform.

Mrs. Karowska was a patient in the local hospital suffering from cancer. Apparently it had started in her throat months before and then spread to her lungs. She suffered much discomfort and pain, and Anya spent a lot of time at her bedside. She finally died a sad, lonely woman full of bitterness and hostility, a stranger even to her only child. There was a proper funeral attended by her friends and conducted by a priest who sent her off with a flowery sermon offering her saintly soul to everlasting peace and heaven. Anya cried bitterly, mostly for all those lost years of never having had a mother when she needed one most.

****

The strange disease that plagued many of the refugees at first had no name. Everyone felt it was just a simple diarrhea caused by the radical change in diet, unsafe water, or simply overindulgence in the fatty corned beef or fruit. Ellie was no exception.

"Mother, how long is this going to last? Every time I swallow the smallest amount of food, or even coffee or water, I immediately get these terrible cramps. They are so bad I break out in a sweat!"

She was stretched out on her mother's cot in the nurses' tent feeling weak and sickly.

"You'd better see a doctor," said one of the nurses, looking Ellie over. "There are quite a few cases of amoebic dysentery reported every day. Is there mucous and blood in your stool?"

Ellie made a face and nodded her head.

"Why didn't you tell me?" Vita was very upset with her.

"I didn't know what it was. I thought it would go away. I am going to see Dr. Helman."

Bernie Helman confirmed the nurse's guess. He explained that the amoeba was a live organism that produced severe irritation and ulceration of the intestines and, if not treated, could sometimes perforate the bowel and cause death.

"Well, isn't that wonderful? What do I do now?" Ellie asked.

"I will see what the hospital has to treat this, but right now you must eat only small portions of rice pap and drink sweetened, boiled water. That bowel has to heal before you can go back to a normal diet. And, Ellie, this is a serious disease. Don't think it will go away all by itself."

"Please don't tell that to mother! I promise to follow your orders. I really want to get over this."

Vita got a whole bag of rice from the kitchen and cooked it on her little fire right outside her tent. Dry cow dung, small sticks and coal briquettes were the only fuel used by the local people, and for a few rubles they would supply quite a bit of it. The rice concoction was terrible. It looked and tasted like glue and Ellie gagged with each swallow. The pills Dr. Helman gave her reduced the cramping somewhat, and after a couple of weeks she started to feel a little better. Some plain, dry toast and weak tea with sugar was added to her "menu," and soon she could begin to eat other foods without the dreaded, painful cramps and the mad dash for the latrines.

How and when am I going to gain some weight, she wondered, looking at her two hip bones sticking out and every rib showing through the skin. Her knees were larger than the thighs and calves and for a sixteen-year-old girl she had no chest whatsoever! Her hair started to grow out a little, curling around her face, but her nose was long, thin and pointy. She tried to remember what she looked like before the war.

"I am sure even my own father wouldn't recognize me," she said to Anya. "How come you haven't changed? You are just as pretty as ever!"

Anya winked mischievously. "That's what married life does for you."

"Sure, that's easy for you to say, but who would want me looking like this?"

The girls laughed and joked, feeling close, like sisters.

"Will you come and visit me when we get home?" Ellie asked.

"That's a promise! I have always wanted to see Switzerland. Is it really as beautiful as they say?"

"Aha, it's the most wonderful place in the whole world!"

****

The effects of long periods of hunger and starvation and subsequent susceptibility to disease were almost more than the hastily put-up field hospitals and the overworked doctors, nurses and other volunteer workers could handle. Food, such as it was, drugs and care were now available to all the refugees, but for many it was too late to reverse the process of slow disintegration of body and mind. Even the ever-present will to live gave in to apathy, loss of memory, and a certain kind of oblivion that was difficult to understand. It was just too late.

It was also too late for the Wozniak's younger daughter Elzunia. The five-year-old no longer responded to anything the doctors, parents and friends were able to do for her. Helman made trip after trip to the large Tashkent hospital looking for advice, drugs, tonics — anything! But it was just too late. The once beautiful little girl was now a wizened, skeletal form on spindly, bony legs with a distended abdomen and huge blue eyes that just stared, questioning, not understanding. She died quietly in her sleep of beri-beri, a strange disease nobody in the group had ever heard of.

****

The children seemed to be least resilient to the effects of starvation. There were so many of them arriving daily from different areas in the Soviet Union, many of them orphans whose parents had perished in the camps or were separated from them during the war. There were so many that the local British authority set up separate housing for small groups and assigned members of the A.T.S. to supervise them.

They were called Yunachki. Ellie and Anya were transferred from their other duties to take care of thirty children housed in a mud adobe just on the edge of JangiJul. They stayed with them seeing to all their needs, supervising their feeding, clothing and some low-key activities. Some of the children were in better health than others, but the mortality rate was overwhelming. Amoebic dysentery, beri-beri, pellagra and denghi fever decimated their numbers. Transport after transport of small bodies was shipped out to local burial grounds.

Vita now had enough freedom and writing supplies to cover scores of pages, pouring out her rage and frustration, writing down all she could observe and learn. This was not to be forgotten, not to be swept under the carpet! The world had to know!

But it was not to be. The world had more important things to do — to fight the Germans and the Japanese and, by all means, not to aggravate their new ally, Stalin, with complaints of mistreatment of millions of civilians. The world had its priorities and this was not one of them!

****

The women and children attached to the Polish 6th Division were scheduled to leave JangiJul in a matter of weeks. Their destination was Krasnovodsk, approximately 1,500 kilometers from Tashkent.

The day finally arrived when long convoys of army lorries left JangiJul and snaked their way through mountainous terrain on narrow, perilous, poorly maintained gravel roads. They were headed for Samarkand, Buchara, and then through the vast plains of the Turkmenistan region to the town of Ashkhabad and eventually Kransnovodsk, a port on the southeastern shore of the Caspian Sea.

They bivouacked along the way, spending two nights under tents hastily put up by the soldiers and were fed British army rations.

Jan Wozniak gathered his "pupils" together during their evening stops and, spreading his map, pointed out all the towns and provinces they were traveling through.

"You children observe as much as you can and learn from this trip," he ordered. "You will probably never have another opportunity to come here again!"

"You can bet on that!" piped up Ellie to the amusement of the others.

"The Caspian Sea is actually a lake, one of the largest in the world. It's a thousand kilometers long and on the southern side it borders Persia. I understand that is where we are headed. When we get there we will finally be beyond the grasp of the evil carrion vine," he exclaimed.

A chorus of cheers broke out with the children clapping their hands. "Imagine going to Persia!"

"Why can't we go home?" the smaller children wanted to know.

"There is a war involving all of Europe right now. The Germans have pushed into Russia this far," he pointed to some of the areas on the map. "Until we defeat them, we can't go back."

"Will you go to war too, Daddy?" asked Krista.

"I certainly hope so. I may be a little old in normal circumstances, but I am an officer and I hope I can still be of some use."

The variety of questions did not come just from the children.
Everywhere, among groups of people, the topic of conversation always was: What next? Where to? Persia was a wonderful prospect, but how could one, relatively small country accept such numbers of people? Where would they put them? How would they feed them? And for how long?

At that point in time there were no answers. Every effort was centered on just getting as many people as possible over the border into a neutral country.

The convoy arrived in Krasnovodsk within three days as planned; and as soon as the lorries were unloaded, they made their trip back to JangiJul to pick up the next group. Krasnovodsk was already set up as a transit camp, and tents covered a huge area close to the sea, and a large number of mud adobes, hastily cleaned and patched up, lined the outskirts of the camp. The group was assigned to one of these "houses" and proceeded to settle down to wait, again, for an undetermined period of time.

****

The main goal of the British / Polish Command was to be able to move all of the Poles over the border to freedom. All of the men and a large number of young women were issued British uniforms and were attached to army units. Ellie signed up with the Auxiliary Transport Service (ATS) and had a picture taken in her new uniform.

THE JOURNEY – 9,000 KILOMETERS

22

THE LAST STEP TO FREEDOM

"...They all stood there, facing the setting sun, straining to see their new home over the calm blue water – a piece of land they would soon stand on as free people..."

On the very first day, while organizing their few possessions, Vita was bitten by a large poisonous scorpion. She and Ellie had picked up a discarded door to use as a picnic table by placing it on top of two wooden crates. She reached under one end of the door and evidently touched the sleeping scorpion who stung her middle finger so painfully that she dropped the door and bent over with pain. Ellie ran to her side and, spotting the scorpion now sitting on top of the door poised for another strike, killed it with a stone.

Dr. Helman was summoned and hastily made arrangements to get Vita to a local hospital for an anti-venom injection to counteract the poison. Her entire hand had swollen very badly, but evidently the serum worked, for she recovered without any ill effects. Everyone was warned to inspect their shoes before putting them on in the morning, never to go barefoot, and also to check all pockets and folds in their clothing. Both scorpions and tarantulas love to hide in dark, warm places. It seemed that this entire area was full of them and the people were frightened half to death of the unfamiliar spiders and snakes they encountered frequently.

They all longed to move on, to get away from the desert, from the sand and dust that irritated their eyes, gritted in their teeth and permeated their clothing. During their entire stay there, not one drop of rain fell on the parched land, promising a very poor harvest of the few kinds of produce grown there. And again, nobody knew exactly how long it would take to ship all the people over to the other side of the sea.

Pahlevi was a Persian port located on the southwestern shore and several barge-like boats sailed back and forth, loaded to capacity with anxious, excited passengers, their eyes fixed on the horizon, looking for signs of land, land that offered them asylum and hospitality.

After several weeks, the day finally arrived for part of the group to board the boats. Ellie and Anya and their troop of children went first, assured by the authorities that the others would follow as soon as more boats became available. Ellie waved to her mother standing on the pier, and a terrible, anxious feeling came over her. What if there wouldn't be any more boats? What if they wouldn't be able to ship the rest of the people? She had an urge to jump overboard and swim back, but Anya hung on to her arm, sensing her friend's anguish.

"This is a mistake," Ellie finally said. "We should never have gotten separated."

The crossing of the Caspian Sea took the better part of the day; and when land was spotted, they all stood there, facing the setting sun, straining to see their new home over the calm blue water — a piece of land they would soon stand on as free people. There were crowds lining the pier as the boats docked, waving and shouting greetings. Ellie and Anya gathered their charges and led them down the boarding plank onto the pier. Anya looked up. Somebody was calling her name!

"Look, it's Jerzy!" Ellie pointed to the young soldier running up the pier.

"I have been meeting every boat. What took you so long?" He lifted her up and twirled her around.

People were hugging each other, crying, laughing, falling to their knees and kissing the ground — free at last!

"Where are Nella and Dorotka?" Jerzy asked, looking for his two little sisters.

"They are with the rest of the group. They should be coming over soon."

"I hope so," Jerzy said, "I would like to see them before my unit leaves."

"When are you going?" Anya asked.

"In a few days. We are moving out to Tehran and from there to Africa to whip the Germans!"

The British authority had finally taken charge of the new arrivals and grouped them all to be transported to their quarters. Tents and warehouses within walking distance from the pier were used for housing. Outdoor kitchens were serving dinner, some kind of mutton stew and rice. Ellie made sure her group of children was fed, washed and put to bed. An A.T.S. captain was in charge of the children's and youths' groups, and Ellie reported to her. She learned that all the orphaned children were to be eventually shipped to England for the duration of the war.

During the next two days, Ellie met every boat that docked in Pahlevi and went back to her tent with a sinking heart. Her mother and some of her other friends were still in Russia and there wasn't any way she could find out when their turn would come. Be patient, she was told. They are all coming over. Finally on the third day, the remainder of the group and patients from the hospital — some ambulatory, some on stretchers under the supervision of Dr. Helman and Vita — sailed into port on the "Kaganovich." Mother and daughter reunited, hung on to each other.

"I was afraid I was never going to see you again!" Ellie said tearfully.

"Sweetheart, I would have gotten here if I had to swim over!"

"Mother, you don't know how to swim!"

They laughed through their tears, happy to be together, looking forward to the next phase of their ordeal, hoping to get back to civilization and eventually find their way home.

****

The End

October 15, 1942
Mother and daughter, reunited, standing at the shore
of the Caspian Sea, Pahlavi, Persia.
FREE AT LAST!!

EPILOGUE

The purpose of this story was to expose the unpublicized fate of all those Poles and others who happened to find themselves in that region of Poland occupied by Soviet Russia on September 17, 1939.

Of course, the story doesn't end here. To satisfy the curiosity of the reader, none of the internees of Camp Vozemka, although safe and out of the Russian borders, was able to return home because of the war which still raged worldwide, and provisions had to be made to repatriate and settle them somewhere until the end of World War II.

The British Government offered them asylum in countries within their Dominion–India, Africa, Australia, and later Canada and the British Isles. And so, phase after phase of depatriation took place starting with the first move to Tehran where the Shah of Iran offered hospitality, lodging and food.

It was here that the small group of friends who had endured so much together over the past two years finally split up. Dr. Helman and his children, the Kucharskis and Mrs. Kos chose to go to Australia; the Wozniaks, the Kews went to India together with Anya and the Czerny girls. Jerzy was sent to the Italian front where he was killed in the Battle of Monte Cassino.

The periods in between these several journeys were of considerable duration, and groups of Polish university professors and various teachers decided to use that time to gather the children and youths and start some kind of education process to make up for the lost time. Youngsters willingly joined the outdoor school, sitting on the ground, under shade trees, listening to lectures on all subjects. The Polish Government in London supplied books and educational outlines and Persian children made little gifts of school necessities.

With each successive leg of their journey, the teachers, classes of children and their parents traveled together, so as not to disrupt the studies. After Tehran, Ahwaz was their next destination, then on to Basra, reputedly the hottest place in the world. An outbreak of typhoid fever claimed many refugees, Ellie among them. She was transferred to an American field hospital in the vicinity of Basra and treated there. Her head was shaved and her 105-degree fever was fought with ice baths.

She recovered and returned to the camp just in time to join her class of students and teachers designated to go to India. This time they traveled by ship through the Persian Gulf, Gulf of Oman and into Karachi, a port on the western shores of

India.

Their stay there was a disaster. It was the monsoon season, and the camp was located along the sandy beaches on the shores of the Arabian Sea. Housing consisted of tents which washed out on several occasions during the heavy, constant rains. Their sleeping cots sat in a foot of water and the humidity was unbearable. Malaria claimed hundreds. Both Vita and Ellie and some of the other members of their group came down with the periodic attacks of chills and fever that were to continue for years to come. The food was also a problem: curried vegetables, rice and chaupatiis were supplied by the people of Karachi, but the food did not agree with the sickly and undernourished bodies. But somehow they survived.

The final phase of their journey, which began in 1939, ended after 9,000 kilometers when a large ship named Santa Yana took them to Bombay and from there to Kohlapur and the close-by camp of Valivade, once used as an Indian army post. Their new quarters were bamboo huts with dirt floors, woven rattan mat walls, screened windows and rope cots with mosquito netting and straw mattresses. Each family was given two small rooms and a kitchen. Staples, fruit and vegetables and Indian buffalo milk were plentiful and, for the first time, each family could prepare its own food.

****

The studies continued. In 1943, twelve girls from Ellie's class were chosen to go to Bombay to submit to an entrance exam for the University of Bombay. The Polish Consul there made arrangements to locate them in a hostel at 7 Pedder Road, Bombay, and a Polish lady, affectionately called "Mama Laskowska," was put in charge of their care. Ellie gained sufficient weight to be seen in a bathing suit without embarrassment, and Vita made frequent visits from Valivade.

The Kews, however, had no news from or about Paul in spite of repeated inquiries through the Polish and Swiss consulates, the International Red Cross, and much correspondence between Vita and her friends and relatives. As far as anybody knew, he just vanished into thin air one day, not to be seen or heard from since.

In 1945, Vita finally learned of Paul's fate. Somehow the pilot of the relief plane was located and reported the deaths of Paul and his two companions.

In 1946, Ellie's junior year, she met a young Swiss chemist who was a member of a Swiss firm in business with the British in Bombay. He was a handsome, engaging young man, fluent in five languages, an accomplished pianist and a fun-loving cut-up. Their marriage did not take place until after Ellie's graduation, at her mother's insistence. Vita finally went home, knowing her daughter was in good hands.

In 1947-48, India gained its independence from the British and all Europeans were asked to leave the country. The couple went home to Switzerland to be reunited with Ellie's mother. Emigration to the United States followed two years later. Vita Kew died in 1965 in her daughter's home in Woodstock, Illinois. She died quietly in her sleep as she always predicted she would — she said God owed it to her.

There are many survivors of the horrendous experience scattered throughout the world with whom Ellic kcpt in touch. Some are in the States, some in Canada, some in Australia, some in Englad and some returned to their native Poland.